THE METALLOIDS

THE METALLOIDS

EUGENE G. ROCHOW

PROFESSOR OF CHEMISTRY
HARVARD UNIVERSITY

D. C. HEATH AND COMPANY

LIBRARY OF CONGRESS CATALOG CARD NUMBER 66-18441

D. C. HEATH AND COMPANY

BOSTON · ENGLEWOOD · CHICAGO · DALLAS
SAN FRANCISCO · ATLANTA

Preface

Descriptive chemistry usually is taught in terms of the metals *versus* the nonmetals, as though that were a natural distinction. The student should be on his guard against such sharply-defined categories, simply because they seldom correspond to reality. He should realize that it is a natural human failing to attempt to classify *everything* into categories, each with its neat label, especially in introductory courses; this stratagem makes it easier to teach a subject and easier to learn it. When he advances to the next step in his search for truth, however, he must be ready to drop the artificial distinctions, or at least to fill in the spaces between them. In this instance, after having learned about metals and nonmetals, it is time to study the metalloids.

This book is concerned with the elements which lie between the true metals and the nonmetallic elements in the Periodic Table and which are called metalloids. They have their own type of behavior, and for precisely that reason they have special uses. Without the metalloids we would have no transistors, no solar batteries, no ceramics, no silicone polymers, no metalloidal biochemical agents, and almost no earth. Hence the subject has extensive theoretical and practical aspects, the scope of which will develop as the plan of the book unfolds.

Chapter 1 reviews the chemical elements which make up our universe and identifies the metalloids among them. The rather sharp physical differentiation of metalloids over metals and nonmetals is then taken up in Chapter 2, followed by a chapter on the general chemical characteristics which are found (in varying degree) in all the metalloids. The succeeding chapters then deal more specifically with the individual metalloidal elements: Chapter 4 with boron and its many peculiarities, Chapter 5 with the well-known and very useful elements silicon and germanium, Chapter 6 with arsenic and antimony (including their therapeutic significance), and Chapter 7 with selenium and tellurium. The practical aspects of all these elements are interwoven with the rest of the text at pertinent places in the exposition, but a special chapter (8) is devoted to the probable, the possible, and even the wish-fathered applications of the metalloids in the future. Since this book is only an introduction to the subject, it is amply documented to help the student probe the more conventional literature. It also contains a special chapter (9) of graded suggestions for further reading about the metalloids.

The book is intended for any serious college student of chemistry who has sufficient curiosity to want to go a little way beyond the usual textbook's delineation and content. It presupposes some knowledge of chemistry and physics but is not a transcribed or translated graduate course. Quite likely it will be used as a supplement to a major conventional course, but there is no reason why a student of chemistry should not pick it up at any time and (hopefully) learn something from it. The writer has tried above all to make it interesting, enjoyable, and relaxed reading, rather than to pound the subject to pulp or powder with facts and figures. Since the book cuts across conventional lines, an attempt has been made to provide an unusually complete index for future reference.

His thirty years of experience undoubtedly have kept the author from being entirely objective about the subject, but he makes no apologies for any outcroppings of personal enthusiasm because he hopes they will help achieve the purpose of the book. He is glad to take full responsibility for any shortcomings that may appear, and to acknowledge his debt to all the colleagues and co-workers in research who helped to provide the background for this effort. He is grateful to Philip K. Blumer and the Dow Corning Corporation, Midland, Michigan, for the photographs and diagrams used in Figures 2.13, 5.0, 5.4, 8.0, 8.1, and 8.2, and for various facts relating to silicon and silicones which Mr. Blumer so kindly provided. And lastly, he is especially grateful to his wife, Helen, who encouraged the writing of the book, typed the entire manuscript, and offered many suggestions to make it more readable and more understandable.

Eugene G. Rochow

Contents

The Metalloid Elements

A metalloid ought to have as much to do with metals as an ellipsoid has with ellipses or celluloid has with cellulose. And it does, except that the ending *-oid* does not indicate "derivation from" but rather has the original meaning of the old Greek suffix, which is "like; resembling; in the form of." Metalloids are solid elements which resemble metals, yet are not completely metallic either in appearance or in properties. They constitute a different class of substances, lying between the metals and the nonmetals in the periodic classification of the elements. Since they have some of the chemical behavior which we associate with the representative metals (such as the formation of organometallic derivatives), and in other ways resemble the familiar nonmetals (in that they form oxides which are acidic, for instance), the metalloids have a rich and varied behavior which gives them a special interest even to the beginning student. Because they are unusual, they also have unique and important uses. One must first understand them from the theoretical standpoint, and then one can understand their nature and their applications.

We can begin by considering the metals and asking why they act the way they do. Everyone knows a metal when he sees one: metals are opaque, shiny, and bendable, and they conduct heat and electricity. Students of chemistry recognize that the metals incorporate a distinctive type of chemical bonding, in which an array of positive ions is held together by an all-pervading sea of electrons, the ultimate in delocalized-electron bonding. Those metals which have only one electron per atom to donate to the common cause (such as sodium and potassium) are weak and soft, and have low melting points; those which contribute two electrons per atom (such as magnesium and calcium) are stronger and have higher melting points. The metals which have the most electrons to contribute to the bonding pool, such as manganese and chromium, are the hardest and toughest. The characteristic shortage of electrons (in relation to the number of orbitals to contain them) places the metallic elements in the left side of the periodic table, where the periods are not fully developed. Furthermore, since heavy elements as a rule have their outermost electrons well shielded from the nucleus (and hence "looser," or more easily detached), the heavier elements in most groups are more metallic in character than the lighter ones.* Hence any dividing line which is intended to set off the metals must be drawn *diagonally* across the periodic table, as in Fig. 1.1.

We may note in passing that the characteristically high electrical conductivity of metals arises from the easy displacement of electrons from one end of a bar or wire to the other, because the electrons are not held in local bonding positions but are free to wander throughout the lattice. The electrons also are free to assume local thermal energies and to distribute any local elevation of temperature throughout the mass, giving rise to the high heat conductivity of metals (and hence the cold feel to the touch). Moreover, the sea of electrons in a metal interacts strongly with incident light, so that the photons of light penetrate only a few layers of atoms before they are scattered outward again—hence the opacity and reflectance typical of metals. We need go no further with the matter here because all these characteristics of metals are considered in more detail in Chapter 2, where theoretical and physical differentiations between the metalloids and the metals are drawn. For the present it will suffice to conclude that the metals are fairly close-knit as a class of substances, and that their properties are fairly well understood in terms of theory.

The opposites of metals are the *nonmetals*, those elements in the upper right-hand corner of the periodic table with high electron affinities and high ionization potentials. These elements, represented

---

* This generality is violated by the sequences Ni-Pd-Pt, Cu-Ag-Au, and Zn-Cd-Hg in the latter part of the transition series, where successive shrinkage and the lanthanide contraction combine to make the atomic radii of platinum, gold, and mercury much smaller than would be expected from the increase in atomic number, and hence the outermost electrons are close to the nucleus and actually are more strongly held than the electrons of their light counterparts nickel, copper, and zinc.

PERIODIC TABLE

Group	Ia	IIa	IIIb	IVb	Vb	VIb	VIIb	VIII			Ib	IIb	IIIa	IVa	Va	VIa	VIIa	0
1st period	1 H																	2 He
2nd period	3 Li	4 Be											5 B	6 C	7 N	8 O	9 F	10 Ne
3rd period	11 Na	12 Mg											13 Al	14 Si	15 P	16 S	17 Cl	18 A
4th period	19 K	20 Ca	21 Sc	22 Ti	23 V	24 Cr	25 Mn	26 Fe	27 Co	28 Ni	29 Cu	30 Zn	31 Ga	32 Ge	33 As	34 Se	35 Br	36 Kr
5th period	37 Rb	38 Sr	39 Y	40 Zr	41 Nb	42 Mo	43 Tc	44 Ru	45 Rh	46 Pd	47 Ag	48 Cd	49 In	50 Sn	51 Sb	52 Te	53 I	54 Xe
6th period	55 Cs	56 Ba	57* La	72 Hf	73 Ta	74 W	75 Re	76 Os	77 Ir	78 Pt	79 Au	80 Hg	81 Tl	82 Pb	83 Bi	84 Po	85 At	86 Rn
7th period	87 Fr	88 Ra	89 Ac															

The Metals

Non-metals

* Lanthanide series

Figure 1.1 Placement of metals, metalloids, and nonmetals in the Periodic System. Metalloids are identified by shaded squares.

so well by oxygen, sulfur, and chlorine, take electrons away from the metallic elements to form negative ions in the well-known metal oxides, sulfides, and chlorides. With each other they form covalent volatile compounds, such as Cl_2O, SO_2, and SO_2Cl_2, in which the bonds are geometrically directed in space and consist of localized pairs of electrons. Only a few of the 103 known elements are nonmetals beyond all dispute—17 of them, in fact, or 1/6 of the total. They occupy the region of the periodic table shown in Fig. 1.1.

Between the regions of the strongly metallic elements and the decidedly nonmetallic ones there is a no-man's land, or zone (indicated in Fig. 1.1), where we may expect to find the metalloids. We can define them a little more closely now as elements which have *some* of the optical and chemical properties of the representative metals, but have distinctly different mechanical and electrical properties. They are distinguished from the typical nonmetals in being always solid, always with at least some metallic luster, and always giving compounds less acidic in character than the corresponding compounds of the nonmetals.

We now seek some quantitative criteria which will enable us to indicate exactly which elements in the broad dividing band of Fig. 1.1 are properly classified as metalloids. There are many quantitative data which may be used to settle this point. For example, we know that the metals vary a great deal among themselves in their propensity to give up electrons in an electrochemical cell, where we take the relative tendency to lose electrons to a 1 M solution of the corresponding ion (in comparison with hydrogen) as the *electrode potential* of the metal. Similarly, the nonmetals vary in their electron acquisitiveness, fluorine being highest in this respect. From these precise measurements we derive the well-known electrochemical series of the elements, which often is used to rank the metals in the order of their chemical metalness.

But some of the elements (silicon and germanium, for example) do not have a well-developed aqueous chemistry, and questions of solubility and hydrolysis obscure the aqueous chemistry of many more. What is more important, chemical reactions can (and do) take place under countless conditions of temperature and pressure other than the arbitrary 25°C and one atmosphere under which electrode potentials are measured, and in the complete absence of water. Hence electrode potentials seem an unnecessarily limited and restrictive basis for ordering the elements according to degree of metallic or non-

4

metallic character, and some other criterion has long been sought.

There really is no single measurement that suits so general and sweeping a purpose, for all require closely-guarded conditions of an arbitrary nature for their determination. Present-day students and teachers usually agree to use *electronegativity* as a compromise criterion, although the concept cannot be defined in a precise way that is backed up by an operational measurement. The best that can be done is to take a variety of physical measurements (such as electron affinity, ionization potential, electrostatic attraction, or heat of formation), each in its appropriate way, and then to combine or contrast the results in such a way as to indicate relative electron-attracting power of the respective elements in their compounds with each other. Fortunately the various methods for arriving at comparative electronegativities show broad areas of agreement, so we are encouraged to use this concept and the resulting figures despite the disapproval of some theorists.

The various methods for calculating electronegativities are considered in detail in many standard references, one of the best being *Advanced Inorganic Chemistry* by Cotton and Wilkinson.* For our purposes we shall make use of the well-known classical electronegativity values of Pauling, which are derived from thermochemical data, and the uniformly consistent but less pragmatic "electrostatic" electronegativities derived from atomic radii and Coulomb's law. These values are given in Table 1.1.

Table 1.1

Electronegativities of the Elements[a]

Element	"Electrostatic" EN	Pauling EN	Element	"Electrostatic" EN	Pauling EN
Li	0.97	1.0	F	4.10	4.0
Be	1.47	1.5	Na	1.01	0.9
B	2.01	2.0	Mg	1.23	1.2
C	2.50	2.5	Al	1.47	1.5
N	3.07	3.0	Si	1.74	1.8
O	3.50	3.5	P	2.06	2.1

[a] A. L. Allred and E. G. Rochow, *J. Inorg. Nucl. Chem.*, **5**, 264 (1958); F. A. Cotton and G. Wilkinson, *Advanced Inorganic Chemistry*, p. 92, Interscience, New York-London, 1962.

---

* Interscience, New York, 1962, page 88 et seq.

Table 1.1 (*continued*)

Electronegativities of the Elements

Element	"Electrostatic" EN	Pauling EN	Element	"Electrostatic" EN	Pauling EN
S	2.44	2.5	Cs	0.86	0.7
Cl	2.83	3.0	Ba	0.97	0.9
K	0.91	0.8	La	1.08	1.1–1.2
Ca	1.04	1.0	Ce	1.06	1.1–1.2
Sc	1.20	1.3	Pr	1.07	1.1–1.2
Ti	1.32	1.5	Nd	1.07	1.1–1.2
V	1.45	1.6	Pm	1.07	1.1–1.2
Cr	1.56	1.6	Sm	1.07	1.1–1.2
Mn	1.60	1.5	Eu	1.01	1.1–1.2
Fe	1.64	1.8	Gd	1.11	1.1–1.2
Co	1.70	1.8	Tb	1.10	1.1–1.2
Ni	1.75	1.8	Dy	1.10	1.1–1.2
Cu	1.75	1.9	Ho	1.10	1.1–1.2
Zn	1.66	1.6	Er	1.11	1.1–1.2
Ga	1.82	1.6	Tm	1.11	1.1–1.2
Ge	2.02	1.8	Yb	1.06	1.1–1.2
As	2.20	2.0	Lu	1.14	1.1–1.2
Se	2.48	2.4	Hf	1.23	1.3
Br	2.74	0.8	Ta	1.33	1.5
Rb	0.89	2.8	W	1.40	1.7
Sr	0.99	1.0	Re	1.46	1.9
Y	1.11	1.2	Os	1.52	2.2
Zr	1.22	1.4	Ir	1.55	2.2
Nb	1.23	1.6	Pt	1.44	2.2
Mo	1.30	1.8	Au	1.42	2.4
Tc	1.36	1.9	Hg	1.44	1.9
Ru	1.42	2.2	Tl	1.44	1.8
Rh	1.45	2.2	Pb	1.55	1.8
Pd	1.35	2.2	Bi	1.67	1.9
Ag	1.42	1.9	Po	1.76	2.0
Cd	1.46	1.7	At	1.96	2.2
In	1.49	1.7	Fr	0.86	0.7
Sn	1.72	1.8	Ra	0.97	0.9
Sb	1.82	1.9	Ac	1.00	1.1
Te	2.01	2.1	Th	1.11	1.3
I	2.21	2.5	Pa	1.14	1.5

Table 1.1 (*continued*)

Electronegativities of the Elements

Element	"Electrostatic" EN	Pauling EN	Element	"Electrostatic" EN	Pauling EN
U	1.22	1.7	Bk	1.22	1.3
Np	1.22	1.3	Cf	1.22	1.3
Pu	1.22	1.3	Es	1.22	1.3
Am	1.22	1.3	Fm	1.22	1.3
Cm	1.22	1.3	Md	1.22	1.3
			No	1.22	1.3

Thorough study of such self-consistent values of electronegativity for all the elements shows that the characteristic *metals* all have electronegativities which lie below 1.8, the alkali metals lying in the range 0.7 to 1.0 and the transition metals in the range 1.11 to 1.75. On the other hand, the elements which commonly are recognized as *nonmetals* have electronegativities between 2.2 (iodine) and 4.1 (fluorine), with oxygen standing at 3.5. In between the metals and nonmetals of Table 1.1 there is a collection of elements of electronegativity 1.8 to 2.2 which are neither metals nor nonmetals, and which are best described as *metalloids*. These are the elements which appear in the shaded band of Fig. 1.1: boron, silicon, germanium, arsenic, antimony, tellurium, polonium, and astatine. Hence we arrive at the same distinction by more quantitative means. We see that the metalloids are not scattered throughout the various groups, but are neatly collected in a compact band which is established by the well-known diagonal relationship within the Periodic System.

For one reason or another, it sometimes is desirable to think of a few other neighboring elements as metalloids. Carbon is one such borderline element; the graphite form conducts electricity, and with a negative temperature coefficient of resistance as do semiconductors. Phosphorus also is included at times, not because of its physical properties (only the rare dense black form is even remotely like a metal in this respect), but because in its lower oxidation states it exhibits an electronegativity within the range of the metalloids. Lastly, on the metallic side of the borderline there lies the heavy, brittle, yellowish metal called bismuth, which has no common nonmetallic form. Since its conductance is only 1.4% that of silver, and since in its amphoteric behavior it often resembles arsenic and antimony, it sometimes is grouped with the metalloids.

What elements are metalloids, then? Certainly boron, silicon, germanium, arsenic, antimony, and tellurium come firmly within our definitions, and these will receive the larger share of attention in this book. In addition, it sometimes will be convenient to include phosphorus, bismuth, and selenium in the discussion. Whether polonium and astatine are (or are not) metalloids is quite immaterial, because they are exceedingly rare and radioactive, and have no utility other than that which depends on their radioactivity.

CHAPTER 2

Physical Differentiation from the Metals

We begin this chapter with a little experiment. Suppose we take a thin bar of nickel and connect it in series with a high-current ammeter to a storage battery or AC transformer, with a sensitive voltmeter connected across the specimen (Fig. 2.1). By increasing the voltage applied to the specimen we find that the current through it (as registered by the ammeter) is directly proportional to the applied voltage, a relation known as Ohm's Law:

$$I \text{ (current)} = \frac{E \text{ (voltage)}}{R \text{ (resistance)}}$$

By taking several readings of I and E, all at constant temperature (we can cool the sample, if necessary, in a nonconducting liquid like pure water), we arrive at a value for R at this temperature. The customary units are defined in such a way that if E is expressed in volts, and I in amperes, R will be in ohms. The actual resistance will depend upon the dimensions of the sample, of course; it will be proportional to length, at fixed cross section, and will be inversely proportional to cross-section area at fixed length, just because of the quantity of material conducting the current. If the nickel is pure, the resistance will correspond to about 8 micro-ohms (8×10^{-6} ohms) for a 1-cm cube. If impurities are present the resistance will be higher, even though the impurities themselves may be better conductors than nickel, such as copper or zinc. An alloy of 19% Ni, 61% Cu, and 20% Zn has a resistance of 33 micro-ohms per cm^3, and an alloy of nickel with chromium and a small proportion of iron has a resistance of 100 micro-ohms per cm^3. This increased resistance is a result of

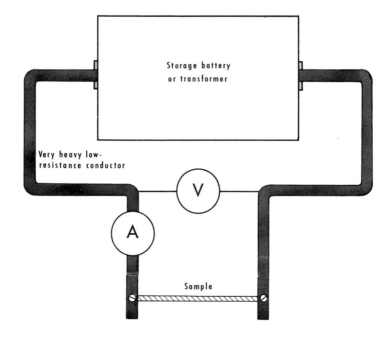

Figure 2.1 Apparatus for electrical conductivity of nickel or silicon.

the formation of intermetallic compounds which interpose a nonuniform lattice in the path of the electrons and so interfere with their free flow throughout the metal. Nonmetallic impurities, such as sulfur or phosphorus, raise the resistance of a metal still more, making necessary the familiar electrolytic refining of copper before it can be used for electrical purposes.

If we continue the experiment of Fig. 2.1 without any provision for cooling, and allow the sample specimen to become heated by the passage of heavy current, its resistance is found to *increase* with rising temperature. Similarly, if the specimen is cooled in liquid nitrogen or a Dry-Ice bath, its resistance decreases. A thermocouple welded to its surface tells us how hot or cold it is, and by making precise measurements we arrive at the relationship shown in Fig. 2.2, where the specific resistance of a 1-cm cube is plotted against temperature in degrees Centigrade. The exponential character of the increase in resistance clearly is evident here, and the temperature coefficient α of the relation $R_t = R_0(1 + \alpha t)$ is +0.006 micro-ohms per degree at 20°C.

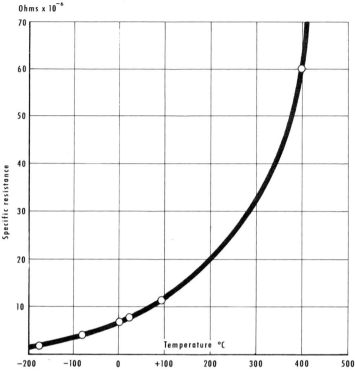

Ohms x 10^{-6}

Specific resistance

Temperature °C

Figure 2.2 Resistance of pure nickel *vs.* temperature.

A similar experiment is now carried out with a chip or sliver of ordinary metallurgical silicon, a shiny blue-gray, crystalline, brittle solid which is about 98.5% Si (with varying amounts of Fe, Al, O, and other elements as impurities). The resistance of the sample rather surprisingly is about the same as that of impure nickel at room temperature, but as the sample heats up (as it soon will do if no provision for cooling is made) the resistance *decreases* and the sample passes more current from a constant-voltage supply. The increased current causes the silicon to heat even more rapidly, which in turn brings about a still lower resistance and allows still more current to flow. The result is a runaway condition which continues until the sample becomes white hot and then melts at about 1400°C. This experiment is both striking and simple; it can be carried out with an ordinary 12-volt storage battery (with cables and battery clips) as a source of current and with a chip of silicon roughly $\frac{3}{4}'' \times \frac{1}{4}'' \times \frac{1}{8}''$ in size selected from the fragments obtained by pounding a 1-lb lump of com-

11

mercial silicon with a hammer. (The silicon costs only about 25 cents, and can be used for a variety of other interesting experiments.)

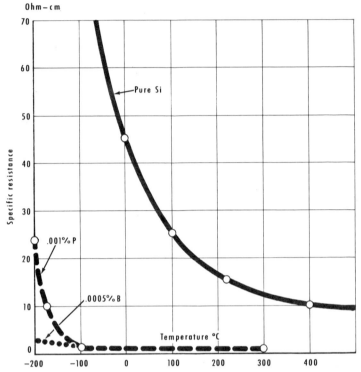

Figure 2.3   Resistance of silicon *vs.* temperature.

Pure silicon is quite another matter, of course; it is quite utterly different in its specific resistance (but not in its behavior *vs.* temperature). A cast bar or rod of refined silicon can be investigated by much the same method as described for nickel, except that a current-limiting device such as a variable-air-gap inductance must be used to prevent the runaway effect. The resulting curve for resistance in plain ohms *vs.* temperature in degrees Centigrade is given in Fig. 2.3, where the negative character of the temperature coefficient is evident. The specific resistance at 25°C for pure silicon is 40 ohm-cm and the temperature coefficient is 1.7 ohm-cm per degree C.

The two examples used in our experiments, nickel and silicon, are representative of two groups of elements to be considered in this chapter: the metals and the metalloids. Not all metals behave in exactly the same way, of course; when we look closely, we see that there are great differences in electrical and thermal conductivity. Some, like silver and aluminum, conduct very well; others, like mercury and chromium, conduct poorly. Below the temperature of liquid hydrogen (20°K) some metals lose all their electrical resistance and become superconductors, as, for example, mercury at 4°K. But above 20°K each metal has a characteristic resistivity and a characteristic temperature coefficient of resistivity, all such coefficients being positive. This general uniformity of electrical behavior must surely have a basis in the structure of metals, and the structure in turn depends upon the arrangement of electrons in atoms of the element and upon the nature of the bonding forces which hold the separate atoms together.

The manner in which metallic bonding arises is of special interest because that bonding is so different from ordinary ionic or covalent bonding. Identical atoms of a metallic element have identically low ionization energies and low electron affinities, and so one atom cannot take electrons away from another. Moreover, the metal atoms have so few unpaired electrons in their outermost atomic orbitals that they cannot enter into hybridized rearrangements (with a single electron in each hybrid orbital) of the sort for which carbon is famous, and hence, they cannot form covalent bonds directed in space like those of carbon. The number of electrons is too small, and the attraction for them is too weak. Instead, the *empty* orbitals of the metal atoms overlap each other extensively, and the few available electrons circulate freely in these massed overlapping orbitals. It is this mobility of electrons in the orbital space that accounts for the high electrical conductivity of the metal, since even a minute difference of potential causes the electrons to drift toward the positive side of the electrical field. Indeed, the number of electrons which will traverse a given path in the metal is proportional to the potential difference, and this is a way of stating Ohm's Law. Notice that the electric current consists solely of a stream of electrons, which are the only carriers. For each electron delivered to the positive pole one enters the metal from the negative pole, and the cores of the metal atoms stay put in their lattice positions.

This same view accounts for the resistance to the flow of an electric current. Such a resistance is in the nature of an interference to the ideally free passage of electrons offered by the heavy constituents of the lattice as they vibrate about mean positions. Since the amplitude of atomic vibration rises with the temperature, all pure metals (without exception!) show increased electrical resistance as the temperature is increased. This is a fundamental difference between metals and semiconductors: all semiconductors *decrease* in electrical resistance when the temperature is raised. Even though semiconductors do their conducting by motion of electrons, just as metals do, the electrons are in a more restricted and localized state of combination in the solid, and they are rendered more mobile by an increase in temperature. The distinction is important, because it turns out that most metalloids are semiconductors; only polonium and the metallic allotrope of antimony show metallic conduction. Hence, even though they may look like metals, the metalloids are distinctly different in internal arrangement. They may have enough free electrons to reflect light the way a metal does, and be about as opaque to short wavelengths, but they act differently in an electrical way.

THEORY

The fundamental differences between metals and semiconductor metalloids can be made clearer by resorting to energy-level diagrams such as have already been encountered by the reader in discussions of atomic spectra. In such diagrams the actual potential-energy function for an electron is simplified by representing it as a square potential well of about the same area (Fig. 2.4). For a single isolated atom the allowable energy levels corresponding to the principal quantum numbers n are drawn in at appropriate heights on the diagram, as shown in Fig. 2.5a. If a diatomic molecule is formed by establishing a covalent bond, the two potential energy wells can be depicted side by side, representing a linear addition of atomic orbitals in what is really a simplification of the corresponding molecular orbitals (Fig. 2.5b). In true metals there is massive overlap of the atomic orbitals in the multi-atom lattice, resulting in such a profusion of low-lying allowable energy levels (Fig. 2.5c) that the few available electrons can circulate freely in these levels. The lines of the atomic energy-level diagram therefore become *bands* when a solid is depicted, and in a metallic solid the bands are numerous but are very sparsely populated because of the chronic shortage of electrons.

We now turn to the metalloids, which have more electrons available per orbital because they are situated further to the right in the periodic table. In a semiconductor like silicon (or in diamond or gray tin) the

14

Figure 2.4 Potential energy of an electron in the vicinity of the nucleus. The
well of width *L* represents
a simple approximation to
the real potential, given by
the curved line. The curve
represents the manner in
which the potential energy
of the electron varies with
distance from the nucleus,
as measured on the hori-
zontal axis.*

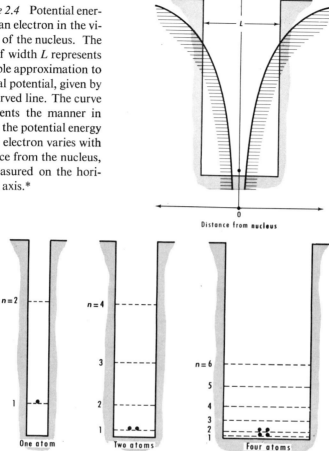

Figure 2.5 An illustration of the simple free-electron model for a metal.
Each atom is pictured as a potential energy well in which the electron is free
to move. The joining together of atoms results in larger potential wells.
The quantized energy levels are lowered in energy and become more closely
spaced. Each allowed energy level is occupied by a maximum of two electrons in accordance with the "Pauli exclusion principle." As the number of
atoms becomes very large, the energy levels become so very closely spaced
that there is essentially a continuum of allowed energies.*

---

*Adapted from Theodore L. Brown, *General Chemistry*, Charles E. Merrill
Books, Inc., Columbus, Ohio, 1963, by permission.

15

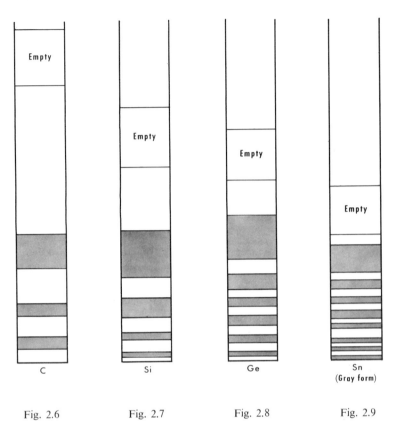

Fig. 2.6   Fig. 2.7   Fig. 2.8   Fig. 2.9

Figures 2.6–2.9   Energy-level diagrams for diamond-lattice elements.

electrons are localized in covalent bonds, and so when we assign electrons two at a time to the available energy levels (in accordance with the Pauli exclusion principle) we find that the lower levels are completely filled. At the same time there are some higher energy levels which are completely empty. Allowing for the usual broadening out of lines into bands, then, we find that solid silicon may be represented by a sequence of filled and empty energy-level bands (Fig. 2.7). Moreover, since diamond, silicon, germanium, and gray tin all have the same crystal structure, they all have a similar pattern of energy-level bands (Figs. 2.6, 2.7, 2.8, and 2.9). The only difference lies in the

16

separation of filled and empty bands and, of course, in the number of bands. In diamond the spacing is wide, and so a great deal of excitation energy is necessary to promote some electrons from the uppermost filled band to the empty band, so that they can migrate freely throughout the lattice and conduct an electric charge. The promotional energy is so large, in fact, that diamond is an insulator at ordinary temperatures, and becomes a semiconductor only at red heat. Silicon, on the other hand, does not hold on to its electrons so strongly, and a few can bridge the gap and be present in the empty bands even at room temperature. It follows that at elevated temperatures more electrons will jump the gap to the empty band, and so there will be more carriers and more conductance in the silicon (Fig. 2.7). Moreover, as substantial numbers of electrons are promoted from a filled band to a hitherto empty band, electron vacancies will be left in the "filled" bands. Electrons from other covalent bonds can move to these vacancies under the stress of an electric field, and other electrons can move into the new "holes." Hence considerable current can be carried by presumed motion of the "holes," and the conductance rises more.

In germanium the spacing between filled and empty bands is still smaller (Fig. 2.8), and so at ordinary temperatures even more conductance electrons have already been promoted to the "empty" bands. Hence the intrinsic conductivity of germanium is greater than that of silicon at 25°C and becomes still higher at elevated temperatures. The trend continues in the allotropic form of tin which has the diamond-structure (usually called gray tin to distinguish it from the bright metallic form, called white tin). In gray tin the energy gap between filled and empty bands is so small that electrons are promoted to the conductance bands in large numbers at room temperature, making the substance a much better conductor than silicon or germanium at that temperature. Indeed, it requires only a moderate rise in temperature to bridge the gap entirely, so that there is no longer any distinction between filled and empty bands and gray tin begins to conduct like a metal.

So it is that semiconductance must always be considered in terms of temperature, and comparisons can be made only at a specified reference temperature. When cooled sufficiently, all semiconductors are insulators, and when heated sufficiently, their electrical behavior merges with that of the metals.

Much more subtle and effective manipulation of the semiconductor properties of the metalloids silicon and germanium is possible by establishing and then controlling a deliberate excess or deficiency of electrons. This is accomplished by introducing minute but carefully-controlled proportions of impurity into a high-quality form of silicon or germanium which has previously been purified to a fantastic degree.* The effect of a particular kind of impurity can best be under-

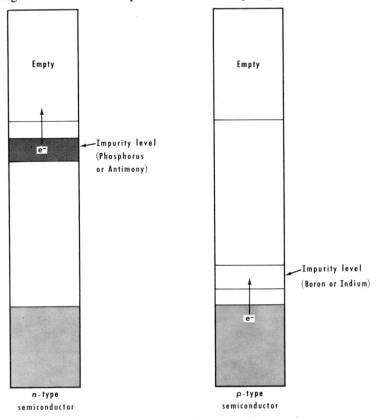

Figure 2.10 Impurity levels in treated germanium.

---

* The purification process starts with an extremely pure source of $SiCl_4$ or $SiHCl_3$, for example, which has been distilled and redistilled until it contains no more than ten or twenty parts per *billion* of boron or phosphorus chlorides. The halide is then reduced to elementary silicon, which is zone-refined to the required purity.

stood by referring to energy-level diagrams again. As is shown in Fig. 2.10, we need not accept only the natural energy-level gap between filled and empty bands in germanium; we can introduce an electron donor which will contribute its own filled band at a level close to the empty band of germanium, or we can introduce an electron acceptor which will contribute an empty band close to a filled band of the germanium. In the first instance an impurity element from Group V is chosen, usually phosphorus or antimony; the atoms of impurity are present in such small proportion (0.001% or so) that they fit right into the diamond lattice of the single crystal of germanium. However, since they have five valence electrons instead of four, an extra electron beyond the four required for the usual four covalent bonds to neighboring atoms becomes available for "promotion" to the conductance band, and since the energy gap between the impurity energy level and the next higher empty level of germanium is small, the extra electrons are easily pushed over the barrier by a potential difference. The result is a large increase in conductivity at room temperature, and one which can be exploited by appropriate control of electrical and mechanical design. Such a semiconductor material is called *n*-type, because the impurity introduces negative carriers of current (electrons).

The other possibility illustrated in Fig. 2.10 involves the introduction of a small proportion of a Group III element, usually boron or indium. Such an element, having only three electrons to contribute to the bonding instead of four, imparts an electron deficiency. If the empty band representing this deficiency lies just above a filled energy-level band of germanium, as is shown, electrons can readily be "promoted" from the filled band by an appropriately large potential difference. The promoted electrons are carriers of current, and also the "holes" left in the previously filled band may move or drift in the field and so carry current. Since the electron-deficient impurity contributes electron holes (or so they are called), and since such sites represent positive charges, the resulting semiconductor material is called *p*-type. Although germanium and silicon (and also most other metalloids, too) are intrinsic semiconductors, their natural conductivity can be increased a thousand-fold or more by adding small amounts of selected impurity in this manner. Solid-state electronic devices employ sensitive semiconductor materials with only 0.0005% or 0.001% of impurity; any more would make the device unnecessarily conductive and too insensitive.* That is why such extreme purity of the metalloid is necessary in the first place.

SOLID-STATE ELECTRONIC DEVICES

Transistors are devices which use *n*- and *p*-type semiconductor material (such as was just described) to amplify and control electric impulses. *Rectifiers* are devices which convert alternating current to direct current, and one type of rectifier also makes use of *n*- and *p*-type semiconductors. The basic principles of operation of rectifiers and transistors can be understood (if the reader has not understood them before) by considering the motions of electrons and "holes" under stress of electric fields. Consider first the simple rectifier shown diagrammatically in Fig. 2.11. This rectifier consists of a "junction" of

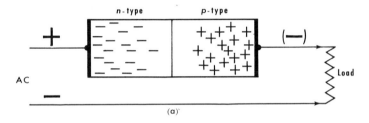

(a)

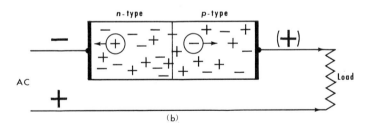

(b)

Figure 2.11 Operation of a semiconductor rectifier.

---

* Notice that metallurgical silicon, as used in the experiment at the beginning of this chapter, has 1% or more of impurity, a gross amount. It ordinarily has no electrical use. As is shown by the scales of Figs. 2.2 and 2.3, the resistance of pure Si is about a million times greater than that of Ni or 99% Si.

n-type and *p*-type silicon or germanium, made either by actually brazing together slices of the right type of crystal or by impregnating a single crystal of metalloid with appropriate impurities at opposite ends. Metal terminals or electrodes are affixed to the ends, and the device is inserted into an alternating-current line so that it may provide direct current for the load instrument or device (here indicated as a simple load resistance). The polarity at the left alternates, of course, as the voltage follows a sine-wave alternation between positive and negative.

When the left electrode of the rectifier is positive, as in the upper diagram (a) of Fig. 2.11, it attracts all the negative carriers (electrons) from the *n*-type semiconductor to it. Similarly, the positive "holes" of the *p*-type semiconductor are attracted to the right-hand electrode, which is negative at that time (being connected to the other AC feed wire through the load resistance). Both actions denude the crystals of their carriers in the vicinity of the junction. Remembering that the semiconductor without extra added carriers has 1000 or more times as much resistance, it is obvious that in this condition very little current will flow across the junction. The device acts just like a high resistance inserted in the line, effectively stopping the current during this part of the AC cycle.

Now consider the opposite condition, indicated in diagram (b) of Fig. 2.11. Here the left electrode is negative, and the right electrode receives a positive charge through the load. Negative carriers (electrons) are repelled from the left and attracted to the right, constituting a current. At the same time, positive carriers (holes) are repelled from the right and attracted to the left, constituting more flow of current. Given enough velocity (by a sufficient potential), both types of carrier pass through the barrier at the junction and transfer charge. Obviously in this condition the device acts like a low resistance, allowing unidirectional current to flow through the load. Then, as the AC potential fluctuates, the rectifier acts as a valve, imposing a high resistance to flow in one direction and a low resistance to flow in the other. In this respect it is a single-wave rectifier, passing the negative pulses but chopping off the positive ones. By arranging two or four such devices in a full-wave rectifying circuit, a more nearly continuous direct current can be supplied to the load.

Many such semiconductor devices are in use today, ranging from radio-circuit diodes which rectify a few microamperes to huge power rectifiers which transmit thousands of amperes. Twenty years ago selenium was used as the semiconductor material; now germanium is used in the small devices and silicon in the large ones. From the preceding diagrams and descriptions, the reader will recognize that silicon is more suitable for high-power applications because it will stand higher inverse peak voltages and will go on operating at higher temperatures than germanium.

We now turn to transistor triodes which operate on the same principles. Consider a sort of double rectifier with *n*-, *p*-, and *n*-type semiconductors arranged in that sequence, as shown in Fig. 2.12.

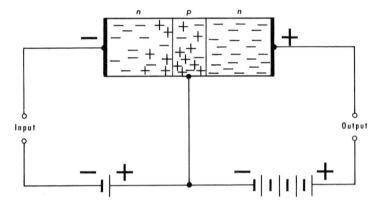

Figure 2.12   Semiconductor metalloids used in a transistor amplifier.

The device is connected to a battery, with a higher voltage on the right-hand junction than the left. Notice that the left-hand junction is biased slightly in the favorable direction, so that electrons and holes cross the barrier freely. Small fluctuations in voltage at the input terminals then produce corresponding changes in current across this first junction. If we imagine the layer of *p*-type material to be very thin, we see that electrons which come flying into it under influence of the input impulses are likely to pass right through it and cross the second barrier. As they do so they are attracted strongly to the right electrode, which bears a relatively high positive charge from the battery. Hence a relatively large current flows through the load device, triggered by swarms of carrier electrons "injected" into the *n*-type semiconductor at the right. It follows that small fluctuations in input voltage produce large changes in current at the load resistance (the output), and the *p*-type material is seen to act as a valve which controls

22

this large current. Hence a weak signal applied at the input terminals is "amplified" in the sense that a faithful but enlarged reproduction of it appears at the output terminals, the increase in power being supplied by the battery.

Since the transistor can be made very small, a short path can be provided for electrons, and the transit time is small. This means that radio-frequency currents can be amplified as well as lower (audio) frequencies, and by using appropriately tuned resonant circuits with the RF transistor amplifier, a radio receiver can be built. The advantages of such a transistor radio are evident to all readers: it is light, compact, and economical. Transistors are much smaller and more durable than the fragile vacuum tubes they replace, and they employ no hot cathode emitters so they need no heater power. In a device where a dozen vacuum tubes would dissipate a great deal of heat and endanger the operation of other components by generating a high temperature, replacement of the tubes with transistors means cooler and more dependable operation as well as a saving of space and power. For these reasons semiconductor devices made of metalloids have achieved great popularity in our time, and their widespread use would provide reason enough for studying the metalloidal elements.

This brief account of the functioning of semiconductor rectifiers and transistors by no means encompasses all the applications of solid-state electronics. There are solar batteries, radiation detectors, variable capacitors, and hosts of other devices made of specially-prepared hyper-pure crystals of the metalloids. Some will be considered in later chapters. As one example of another solid-state device which has taken over a function previously performed by a fragile glass tube (a Geiger counter), see Fig. 2.13.

OPTICAL BEHAVIOR

Even though they look metallic and have a metallic luster in various shades of gray (from bluish chromium color to yellowish bismuth color), the metalloids differ from the typical metals in their optical properties. The differences in bonding which were emphasized earlier in this chapter operate to give fewer *free* electrons in the metalloids than in true metals, and so there is less interaction with visible and infrared radiation. Germanium is quite transparent to the far infrared, and is used for windows in spectrographic equipment intended for those frequencies; it transmits more far-infrared energy than quartz,

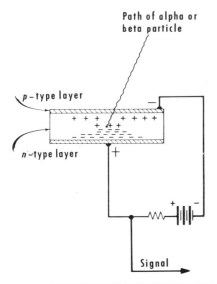

Path of alpha or
beta particle

p –type layer

n –type layer

Signal

Figure 2.13 **King-size** radiation detector. An alpha or beta particle creates a charge as it strikes the detector. A bias voltage across the silicon slice removes the charge as an electrical signal to the detector circuit.

24

for example. The other metalloids differ widely in their optical behavior, but none of them reflects visible and infrared radiation as well as aluminum or silver.

One way of achieving quantitative comparisons of the optical properties of solid metalloid elements and their binary compounds is to consider their refractive indices. The index of refraction of a substance is the ratio of the velocity of light in vacuum to its velocity in that substance:

$$\text{index of refraction } n = \frac{v_o}{v}$$

According to electromagnetic theory,* the index of refraction should also be equal to the square root of the dielectric constant of the medium at the same frequency, the dielectric constant ϵ being the ratio of electric-charge storage in the material to charge storage in vacuum (i.e., in the same capacitor with no material between the plates). With this relationship, dielectric measurements can also be brought into the discussion (a matter of some convenience, since it sometimes is easier to measure dielectric properties than optical). Table 2.1 lists some of these constants for a few typical metalloids and binary compounds.

Table 2.1

Index of Refraction and Dielectric Constant

Substance	% Reflection	n_D	Dielectric Const., ϵ
Diamond	6	2.417	16.5 with DC
Si	41	4.39	12.5
SiC	—	2.65–2.69	50 at 30 kc
Ge	35	4.1	16.0
As	46	3.54	10.2 at 60 cy
Sb	70	3.04	—
Se	—	2.92	6.13
Te	59	3.07	—
Crown glass	4	1.520	6.96 with DC
NaCl	4	1.544	6.12 at 10 kc

* See, for example, the development in F. K. Richtmyer, E. H. Kennard, T. Lauritsen, *Introduction to Modern Physics*, McGraw-Hill Book Co., New York, 1955.

It is notable that the metalloids of Table 2.1 all are much more highly refractive than glass or rock salt, and even somewhat more refractive than diamond. Dispersion, which is change of refractive index with wavelength, is also very marked, so much so that the $n = \sqrt{\epsilon}$ relation does not hold whenever the two properties are measured at different frequencies. The high refraction and dispersion of germanium, for example, coupled with its transparency in the infrared, would allow lenses and prisms to be made of it for use in IR spectrographs. Silicon absorbs more infrared energy, and also absorbs ultraviolet and visible light sufficiently well to enable its use in solar cells and batteries such as those which power the radio transmitters in satellites.

MECHANICAL PROPERTIES

Although some metals are brittle, most are malleable and ductile, and some are very strong and tough. The metalloids, on the other hand, are all brittle; instead of deforming under stress, they resist a force elastically up to the point of shattering. Nevertheless, some metalloids are extremely hard. Table 2.2 gives some pertinent mechanical properties.

Table 2.2

Mechanical Properties of Metalloids

Substance	Moh Hardness	Young's Modulus	Compressive Strength	Compressibility, v/v_0
B	9.3	—	very high	0.00004[a]
Si	7.0	10890	947 kg/mm^2	0.00491[a]
SiC	9.15	4500	18,600	0.00002[b]
As	3.5	—	—	0.0119[a]
Ge	6.0	8000	—	0.0062[a]
Se	2.0	5912	—	—
Te	2.3	4200	—	0.0051[a]

[a] At 70,000 lbs per sq in
[b] At 500 atmospheres

Although silicon carbide has many uses that depend upon its hardness, and a few uses (such as that for supports in ceramic kilns) that depend upon its strength at high temperatures, the *elementary* metal-loids are not famous or useful for their mechanical properties. The *optical* properties of silicon and selenium are essential to their use in photocells and solar batteries, of course. It is in the area of *electrical* behavior that the metalloids achieve their greatest utility, and so it is in this area that physical distinction over the metals becomes most important.

C H A P T E R **3**

Chemical Characteristics

As is inherent in the definition of a metalloid given in Chapter 1, and is expected from the electronegativities of the elements under consideration, the metalloids have chemical properties which are intermediate between those of representative metals and representative nonmetals. This is just to say that metalloids do not have a unique or distinctive chemical behavior, but take places in the gradual change from basic (metallic) behavior to acidic (nonmetallic) behavior. Their oxides are weakly but definitely acidic, and their halides are volatile, covalent substances rather than salts.

This brief paragraph does not tell the entire story, of course, because it is too heavy with generality. In the first place, there is no particular element that can be called a representative metal, and certainly no representative nonmetal. For example, aluminum is a strongly electropositive, very reactive metal with a high electrode potential, and yet it is amphoteric; so are the metalloids. The halogens are arch-nonmetals, and iodine is a halogen, yet iodine forms weak bonds to hydrogen and its hydride is strongly reducing; so are those of the metalloids. A little more study of detail is necessary in order to understand the situation, and so some of the principal classes of compounds will be considered.

HALIDES

Although the halides of the alkali and alkaline-earth metals are salts, those of the Group III metals and most of the transition elements are quite covalent and rather volatile (witness $TiCl_4$, a volatile, colorless liquid, and CrO_2Cl_2, a liquid boiling at 117°C; $CrBr_3$ and $FeCl_3$, sublimable solids; $AuCl_3$, $PtCl_4$, $RuCl_3$, and Hg_2Cl_2, nonionic covalent solids). The halides of the metalloids fit in with this majority, but extend much further in the direction of volatility, some being gases. At the same time the bonds to halogen elements are strong, and the molar heats of formation of some of the halides (such as those of BF_3, BCl_3, and SiF_4) are among the highest known. Table 3.1 lists some compounds which will serve as examples.

Table 3.1

Some Halides of the Metalloids

Compound	Mp, °C	Bp, °C	ΔH_f, kcal/mol
AsF_3	−8.5	63	—
AsF_5	−80	−53	—
$AsCl_3$	−18	130	72.4
$AsBr_3$	32.8	221	46.4
SbF_3	292	subl.	216.5
SbF_5	7.0	149	—
$SbCl_3$	73.4	223	91.4
$SbCl_5$	2.8	140	107.3
$SbBr_3$	96.6	280	61.4
BF_3	−127	−101	256.9
BCl_3	−107	12.5	89.1
BBr_3	−46	90.1	42.8
SeF_4	−135	93	—
SeF_6	−39	34.5	—
$SeCl_4$	305	288 dec.	46.2
SiF_4	−77	−65 at 181 mm	361
$SiCl_4$	−70	57.6	149
$SiBr_4$	5	153	91.5
SiI_4	120	290	27.8
TeF_4	130	—	—
TeF_6	−36	−35.5	—
$TeCl_2$	209	327	—
$TeCl_4$	224	414	77.4
$TeBr_2$	210	339	—
$TeBr_4$	380	421	—

Inspection of the table shows that the higher fluorides AsF_5, SbF_5, and TeF_6, despite their greater molecular weights, have lower melting and boiling points than the lower fluorides AsF_3, SbF_3, and TeF_4. This is explained not just by saying that "fluorine lends the other elements wings," or by pointing to the derivation of the name *fluorine*, but rather is a consequence of the fact that all metals and metalloids become less electropositive in their higher oxidation states. Electrons are lost (or are contributed to sigma bonds) with increasing difficulty as their numbers mount, leading to less metallic character and decreased polarity of the bonds to halogen atoms. In other words, the higher fluorides approach more closely the homopolar covalent state which leads to low intermolecular attraction.

The high heats of formation of boron trifluoride, antimony trifluoride, and silicon tetrafluoride are noteworthy. These halide compounds rank among the most stable ones known (compare sodium fluoride, 136 kcal, and sodium chloride, 98 kcal). At the same time, all three are highly reactive and hydrolyse readily. Boron trifluoride fumes in moist air and forms fluoroboric acid in liquid water:

$$2\,BF_3 + 3\,H_2O \text{ (vapor)} \rightarrow \underline{B_2O_3} + 6\,HF \text{ (vapor)}$$

and, with more moisture available

$$BF_3 + 3\,H_2O \text{ (vapor)} \rightarrow \underline{B(OH)_3} + 3\,HF \text{ (vapor)}$$

But in liquid water, which captures the hydrogen fluoride in hydrated form and builds up a concentration of hydrofluoric acid, an equilibrium is reached with incoming boron trifluoride

$$BF_3 + HF \rightleftharpoons HBF_4$$

Similarly, silicon tetrafluoride fumes in moist air as it forms silicon dioxide

$$SiF_4 + 2\,H_2O \text{ (vapor)} = SiO_2 + 4\,HF \text{ (vapor)}$$

but in limited liquid water it comes to equilibrium as fluorosilicic acid

$$SiF_4 + 2\,HF \rightleftharpoons H_2SiF_6$$

If bases are present, salts of fluoroboric acid and fluorosilicic acid are formed, but in the absence of base the indicated equilibria persist. It follows that silicon dioxide is soluble in solutions of hydrofluoric acid, even if quite dilute. (Boric oxide is somewhat soluble even in water alone, but is much more soluble in hydrofluoric acid.) The chlorides BCl_3 and $SiCl_4$ also fume strongly in moist air

$$BCl_3 + 3\,H_2O \text{ (vapor)} \rightarrow \underline{B(OH)_3} + 3\,HCl \text{ (vapor)}$$

$$SiCl_4 + 2\,H_2O \text{ (vapor)} \rightarrow \underline{SiO_2} + 4\,HCl \text{ (vapor)}$$

and act exactly the same way in liquid water because they form no complexes with chloride ion. It follows that SiO_2 is *not* soluble in hydrochloric acid, nor in hydrobromic or hydroiodic acids. The larger elements differ in that they may accommodate more chlorine atoms around them, and so some chlorogermanates are known.

The fifth-group metalloids differ in that the oxides formed by hydrolysis are in themselves amphoteric, and so a more general reversibility obtains

$$SbCl_3 + 3\,H_2O \rightleftharpoons \underline{Sb(OH)_3} + 3\,HCl$$

and then

$$Sb(OH)_3 + 3\,NaOH \rightleftharpoons Na_3SbO_3 + 3\,H_2O$$

or

$$Sb(OH)_3 + 3\,HCl \rightleftharpoons SbCl_3 + 3\,H_2O$$

In addition to this hydrolytic behavior, which is only one aspect of a general reactivity toward hydroxy compounds, all the trihalides and tetrahalides listed in Table 3.1 are Lewis acids in varying degree. All can accept additional halogen or hydrogen halide reversibly

$$BF_3 + HF \rightleftharpoons HBF_4$$

or

$$BF_3 + F^- \rightleftharpoons BF_4^-$$

or

$$SbF_3 + F_2 \rightleftharpoons SbF_5$$

and so all are Lewis acid catalysts to some extent. Because of the small size of the boron atom, the complement of only six electrons around it, and the extreme electronegativity of the fluorine atoms, boron trifluoride is by far the strongest Lewis acid of the group, and is used as a hydrocarbon-soluble acid catalyst in petroleum alkylation as well as in many other industrial processes. Similarly, a mixture of antimony trifluoride and pentafluoride is used as a fluorination catalyst because it is a fluorine carrier. As for the exception, in selenium hexafluoride the selenium is up to its maximum covalency* and cannot

---

* The concept of covalency maxima was advanced by N. V. Sidgwick in the 1930's to explain the inertness of CF_4 vs. SiF_4, and of SF_6 vs. SF_2 and SF_4. Maximum covalency of the first period is 2, of the second period 4, of the third and fourth periods 6, and of the others 8.

act as an electron acceptor. Like sulfur hexafluoride, it has no acid properties (and very little reactivity).

What has been said about hydrolysis applies in similar fashion to ammonolysis, and to reaction with any basic substance. For example, boron trichloride reacts vigorously with methanol to form methyl borate and liberate hydrogen chloride

$$BCl_3 + CH_3OH \rightarrow B(OCH_3)_3 + 3\,HCl$$

This is seen to open the way for many organic derivatives of the metalloids in which the metalloid element is linked through oxygen to carbon. Hundreds of such derivatives are known, many of them useful. The important point to be made here is that in such reactions the metalloids again show a decidedly amphoteric behavior. For just one example, silicon tetrachloride reacts with organic bases like methyl amine

$$SiCl_4 + 4\,CH_3NH_2 \rightarrow Si(NHCH_3)_4 + 4\,HCl$$
$$\text{(followed by } HCl + CH_3NH_2 \rightarrow CH_3NH_3Cl)$$

and with organic acids such as acetic acid or its anhydride

$$SiCl_4 + 4\,CH_3COOH \rightarrow Si(OOCCH_3)_4 + 4\,HCl$$
$$SiCl_4 + 4\,(CH_3CO)_2O \rightarrow Si(OOCCH_3)_4 + 4\,CH_3COCl$$

Such reactions are helped along their way by the strong affinity of the metalloids for oxygen, which is the subject of the next section.

OXIDES

The amphoteric nature of the oxides of the metalloid elements has already been stressed, and every student of chemistry is familiar with borates, silicates, germanates, arsenates, and antimonates (and, by analogy to sulfates, probably with selenates and tellurates as well). The most important point at present is not just that there are oxides or that they are amphoteric, but that much energy often is liberated in the formation of metalloid-oxygen bonds and that this fact governs much of the chemical behavior of the elements and their hydrides, halides, nitrides, and similar binary compounds. Table 3.2 lists a number of representative oxides, together with their heats of formation.

32

Table 3.2

Physical Properties of Oxides of the Metalloids

Compound	Mp, °C	Bp, °C	ΔH_f, kcal/mol
B_2O_3 cryst.	294	1500	279.8
SiO_2, quartz	1470	2230	201.3
GeO	710 subl.	—	—
GeO_2	1115	—	—
As_2O_3	315	193 subl.	147.9
As_2O_5	315 dec.	—	217.9
Sb_2O_3	656	1550	165.4
Sb_2O_5	380 dec.	930 dec.	230.8
Bi_2O_3	820	1890	135.5
SeO_2	345	316 subl.	56.4
SeO_3	120 dec.	—	—
TeO_2	red heat	450 subl.	78.3
TeO_3	600 dec.	—	83.2

The oxides of boron, silicon, and germanium can readily be obtained in *vitreous* form by melting the crystalline varieties and chilling the melts. In the vitreous form their physical properties are different from those of the crystalline forms, of course, and the vitreous oxides are slightly more reactive and more soluble in water. All three oxides fuse with each other and with Li_2O, Na_2O, CaO, MgO, K_2O, Al_2O_3, BaO, and ZnO to make the many kinds of glass which are produced commercially. In general, the introduction of a light element like lithium decreases the density and refractive index of the vitreous metalloid oxide, and conversely the introduction of barium or lead makes the glass more dense and more refractive. At the same time, the *dispersion* of a glass (which is the change of refractive index with wavelength) varies sharply with composition, and can be quite different for two glasses of different composition even though the two are matched for the same index of refraction at some reference wavelength. It is this difference in dispersion which allows multi-component lenses for cameras and microscopes to be designed in such a way as to eliminate chromatic aberration. Conversely, multi-component prisms for direct-vision spectroscopes have similarly-chosen types of glass arranged in such a way as to correct for all refraction but achieve maximum *dispersion* of the light that enters. These and many other fascinating aspects of glass composition and technology make good collateral reading* for a student of chemistry, for the common glasses can all be considered to be solutions of metal oxides in a non-aqueous solvent composed of oxides of the metalloids, with all the consequent aspects of solubility, coordination, oxidation state, and redox potential which are so important to inorganic chemistry.

The oxides of the metalloids of Groups III, IV, and V (as exemplified by the first nine entries of Table 3.2) all have high heats of formation, and their relationship with oxygen tends to dominate all of their inorganic and mineral chemistry. Whenever a bond to oxygen can form, it will do so, at the expense of bonds to chlorine, bromine, iodine, nitrogen, sulfur, or any other electronegative element except fluorine. As we have seen, M-F bonds are comparable in strength to M-O bonds (where M represents a metalloid), and since fluoride ions also are good complexers, fluorides of the metalloids behave differently and so constitute a separate class.

All the other compounds of the metalloids MX_a (where X is an electronegative element) may be expected to hydrolyse, oxidize, or react in any other way that will produce M-O bonds. A great variety of oxyacids and their ions is the result, embracing most natural minerals and rocks, plus all of ceramic chemistry and even parts of metallurgy. These compounds also are important in the commercial preparation of phosphors, detergents, silicate adhesives, pigments, and silicone polymers. Selenium and tellurium form weaker bonds to oxygen, and consequently have a much more meager oxyacid chemistry.

HYDRIDES

A further differentiating characteristic of the metalloid elements is that they form volatile hydrides. In this respect they are like oxygen, sulfur, chlorine, nitrogen, and the other electronegative elements, instead of like the Group Ia and Group IIa metals (which form saltlike hydrides) or the transition metals (which form interstitial or metallic hydrides). At the same time, the hydrides of the metalloids are more distinctive in structure and more varied in reaction than those of the negative elements. This is especially true of the hydrides of boron, which will be described in some detail in Chapter 4. The other

---

* See, for example, the article on glass in the *McGraw-Hill Encyclopedia of Science and Technology*, Vol. 6, p. 206, and the references which follow it.

hydrides are gases or low-boiling liquids of rather low thermal stability. They are highly reducing in chemical behavior, and are dominated by the relationship of oxygen with the metalloids, as just described. A representative listing appears in Table 3.3.

Table 3.3

Some Hydrides of the Metalloids

Compound	Mp, °C	Bp, °C	ΔH_f, kcal/mol
B_2H_6	−165.5	−92.5	6.7
B_4H_{10}	−120.0	17.6	—
B_5H_9	−46.6	0 at 66 mm	—
B_5H_{11}	−123.4	65	—
B_6H_{10}	−65.1	0 at 7.2 mm	—
$B_{10}H_{14}$	99.7	213 extrap.	—
SiH_4	−185	−112	11.9
Si_2H_6	−132.5	−14.5	—
Si_3H_8	−117.4	52.9	—
Si_4H_{10}	−93.5	80	—
GeH_4	−165	−90	—
Ge_2H_6	−109	29	—
Ge_3H_8	−106	110	—
AsH_3	−113.5	−55	43.5
SbH_3	−88.5	−17	34.3
BiH_3	—	22	endothermic
SeH_2	−64	−42	15.8
TeH_2	−51	−4	33.9

The reactivity of M-H bonds toward oxygen is aptly illustrated by the fact that the simplest hydrides of boron and silicon burst into flame as soon as they are exposed to air. All the hydrides are strong reducing agents, and will precipitate the metals from solutions of heavy metal salts, such as silver nitrate or mercury dichloride. They also are destroyed by strong oxidizing agents like potassium permanganate and sodium dichromate in acid solution.

Hydrolysis is a violent reaction for the hydrides of boron and silicon, but monogermane, GeH_4, is comparatively indifferent to water, as are the hydrides of some other rather electronegative ele-

35

ments.* As a convenient consequence, GeH_4 can readily be prepared by the action of sodium borohydride on a water suspension of GeO_2, the hydride bubbling out of the water quite unharmed. All the hydrides which come before GeH_4 in Table 3.3 must be prepared under *strictly* anhydrous conditions, as in a vacuum train. In fact, most vacuum-train techniques for preparing, purifying, and analysing sensitive chemical substances were developed by Alfred Stock in the 1920's as necessities during his pioneering work on the boron hydrides. The synthesis of such hydrides is now an easier matter than it was in Stock's day, however, because lithium aluminum hydride, $LiAlH_4$, a commercially available reagent discovered by Herman Schlesinger and his coworkers in the 1940's, reduces all halides of boron, silicon, germanium, arsenic, etc. to hydrides.

One more characteristic of the hydrides of the metalloids is distinctive and important: they add to the double bonds of alkenes and the triple bonds of alkynes to form organic derivatives (or metalloid-substituted hydrocarbons, depending on how you look at it). Such addition reactions are favored by the presence of strongly negative groups or atoms on the metalloid atom, as in the classical example of the addition of trichlorosilane to ethylene:

$$HSiCl_3 + H_2C{=}CH_2 \xrightarrow[\substack{\text{or peroxides,}\\ \text{or Pt}}]{\text{UV light,}} CH_3CH_2SiCl_3$$

The significance of such reactions will be understood better in the context of the next section.

ORGANOMETALLIC COMPOUNDS

Hydrocarbon derivatives of the metals have played an important part in inorganic chemistry for over a century,** and since the earliest days the metalloids have figured prominently in those developments. In fact, the earliest *classical* organometallic compounds (which are what we would now call sigma-bonded carbon derivatives, as opposed to pi-bonded ones) were some very poisonous methyl compounds of

---

* See Cotton and Wilkinson, *Advanced Inorganic Chemistry*, p. 92, Interscience, New York, 1962, for a discussion of this and other electronegativities. In its chemical properties germanium acts very much like arsenic.

** See E. G. Rochow, *Organometallic Chemistry*, Selected Topics in Modern Chemistry, Reinhold, New York, 1964.

arsenic prepared by Robert Bunsen in 1841. The term "organo-metallic" traditionally embraces both metals and metalloids, because in this area of chemistry the metalloids stand squarely with the metals. This can best be illustrated by pointing out some details of the preparation of organometallic compounds and some of their chemical behavior.

Let us consider first that method for preparing organometallic compounds which is known as the Direct Synthesis. In this preparative method a hydrocarbon or a hydrocarbon halide reacts directly with the metal or metalloid of interest, forming one or more carbon-to-metal bonds and producing the desired organometallic substance without the use of any other reagent. At the time of writing, some 34 elements are known to participate in this reaction, each requiring conditions which are particularly appropriate. For example, a dispersion of lithium in mineral oil reacts with a solution of butyl chloride in a hydrocarbon solvent at 30°C

$$2 \text{ Li} + \text{n—C}_4\text{H}_9\text{Cl} \rightarrow \text{n—C}_4\text{H}_9\text{Li} + \underline{\text{LiCl}}$$

to make a very useful reagent commonly employed in organic chemistry. Similarly, aluminum reacts with ethyl chloride, using excess reagent plus product (both in the liquid phase) as solvent:

$$2 \text{ Al} + 3 \text{ C}_2\text{H}_5\text{Cl} \xrightarrow[65°C]{(\text{C}_2\text{H}_5)_3\text{Al}} \text{C}_2\text{H}_5\text{AlCl}_2 + (\text{C}_2\text{H}_5)_2\text{AlCl}$$

As another example of a direct synthesis in a liquid medium, magnesium reacts with bromo- or iodo-alkanes in diethyl ether to form the well-known Grignard reagent

$$\text{Mg} + \text{CH}_3\text{Br} \xrightarrow[35°C]{(\text{C}_2\text{H}_5)_2\text{O}} \text{CH}_3\text{MgBr}$$

On the other hand, all the metalloids* react with simple alkyl halides

RX *without any solvent* to produce compounds of the type RMX:

$$2 \text{ CH}_3\text{Cl} + \text{Ge} \xrightarrow[\text{Cu catalyst}]{320°C} (\text{CH}_3)_2\text{GeCl}_2$$
$$\text{(plus some CH}_3\text{GeCl}_3$$
$$\text{and a little (CH}_3)_3\text{GeCl)}$$

$$3 \text{ CH}_3\text{Br} + 2 \text{ As} \xrightarrow[\text{Cu catalyst}]{340°C} (\text{CH}_3)_2\text{AsBr} + \text{CH}_3\text{AsBr}_2$$

---

* The tightly bound crystals of elementary boron require a very high temperature of reaction to tear the atoms loose, and consequently extensive decomposition of the products takes place. The reaction is under study at the time of writing.

$$2\,C_6H_5Cl + Si \xrightarrow[\text{Ag catalyst}]{450°C} (C_6H_5)_2SiCl_2$$

(plus some $C_6H_5SiCl_3$,
a little $(C_6H_5)_3SiCl$,
some $SiCl_4$, and traces of
many other products)

These direct reactions now are the chief sources of the thousands of tons of organometalloidal products made each year for polymers, insecticides, fungicides, and plastics additives.

The organometalloidal halides themselves are almost never the end products for these uses, but rather are intermediates which are hydrolysed or otherwise processed to obtain the required compositions (some of which will be treated in subsequent chapters). A halide of the type $R_aMX_{(b-a)}$ (where b is the normal bonding capacity of M, and a is a smaller integer) hydrolyses or solvolyses just the way the corresponding halide MX_b does, though not as vigorously:

$$4\,(CH_3)_2GeCl_2 + 8\,NaOH \xrightarrow[\text{HC solvent}]{H_2O\ and} [(CH_3)_2GeO]_4 + 8\,NaCl + 4\,H_2O$$

and

$$4\,(CH_3)_2SiCl_2 + 12\,NH_3 \xrightarrow[\text{solvent}]{CH} [(CH_3)_2SiNH]_4 + 8\,NH_4Cl$$

It is through these simple reactions that the products of direct synthesis find use.

In addition to the direct syntheses in which all the metalloids participate, various *replacement reactions* may also be used to prepare alkyl or aryl derivatives of the metalloids. In this scheme of preparation, an alkyl or aryl derivative of some active metal such as lithium or sodium or magnesium first is prepared, and this organometallic reagent transfers its organic groups to the metalloid by subsequent reaction. Such preparations usually are carried out using organolithium or Grignard reagents as the alkylating agents, and of course a solvent is necessary.

$$SnCl_4 + 4\,C_6H_5Na \rightarrow (C_6H_5)_4Sn + 4\,NaCl$$

$$(CH_3)_2SiCl_2 + 2\,C_4H_9Li \rightarrow (CH_3)_2Si(C_4H_9)_2 + 2\,LiCl$$

$$BiBr_3 + C_2H_5MgBr \rightarrow C_2H_5BiBr_2 + MgBr_2$$

These replacement reactions follow some guiding principles known as Gilman's Rules, by which an organometallic reagent of some metal *more* active than the subject metal is necessary as an alkylating reagent, simply because a reagent of some less active metal will not be able to

38

transfer its alkyl groups. Since all the customary convenient alkylating reagents (such as the Grignard reagent) employ metals far more active than the metalloids we have been considering, this is no problem in practice. Substitution reactions of this sort are still used extensively to prepare organic derivatives of the metalloids, especially when complicated organic groups unsuitable for a direct synthesis are to be transferred.

Lastly, let us consider briefly the olefin addition reaction mentioned in the previous section. The addition of Ge-H bonds to ethylene follows exactly the same course as the addition of Al-H bonds of AlH_3 or R_2AlH to ethylene in the Ziegler synthesis, but with a free radical R· as initiator:

$$\diagdown\!\!Al\!-\!H + H_2C\!\!=\!\!CH_2 \xrightarrow[\text{pressure}]{\text{ca. }100°C,} \diagdown\!\!AlCH_2CH_3$$

and

$$-\!Ge\!-\!H + H_2C\!\!=\!\!CH_2 \xrightarrow[\text{pressure}]{60°C + R·,} -\!GeCH_2CH_3$$

Tin hydrides add without catalysts, just as aluminum hydrides do, and so will germanium and silicon hydrides if heated sufficiently in an autoclave. However, free-radical catalysts or finely-divided platinum will greatly speed up the addition of Si-H and Ge-H compounds at moderate temperatures.

To summarize, in all these prototype reactions by which organometalloidal compounds are made and used, we have seen direct parallels with analogous reactions employing common and typical metals. Hence we may say that in this area of chemistry the metalloids are safely grouped with the true metals. In the area of the binary oxides and halides, the metalloids act as extensions of the well-known activity series of metals in the direction of lower activity and less electropositive character. In the area of the hydrides, the metalloids stand quite apart from the true metals, forming hydrides of distinctive structure, properties, and reactions.

CHAPTER 4

Something Special About Boron

THE ELEMENT

Boron was known to the alchemists, but it is still something of a mystery today. All the light elements are highly individualistic, but this one is special. Its combination of small size and relatively high positive field intensity leads it to hold on to its few electrons tenaciously, so that it is not metallic in its behavior. Furthermore, with only one electron in its $2p$ orbitals it is a strong electron acceptor; even if its three exterior electrons are spread out in sp^3 orbitals, and three covalent bonds are formed, the boron atom still has room for a fourth pair of electrons and will attract them strongly. (Aluminum, the second Group IIIa element, having another completed shell between its nucleus and its valence electrons, does not exercise the same attraction and therefore acts as a conventional metal.) Boron is so extreme in its behavior that it really constitutes a different *kind* of element, one which does not follow the usual rules for chemical combination nor fall into easy generalizations. The element and most of its compounds have been a puzzle to theoreticians for many years, and although each generation of chemists has claimed some triumphs of understanding, boron still presents more challenges than any other familiar element.

The name "boron" is an English adaptation of the Persian *burah* given by alchemists about 800 A.D. to borax, $Na_2B_4O_7 \cdot 10\ H_2O$. The element itself first was separated by Davy a thousand years later (in 1807), but Davy's boron was contaminated with suboxides and gave no indication of the physical properties of the pure element.

For a long time "elementary boron" meant the brown amorphous powder of variable composition (80 to 90% B) obtained by the Moissan process of reducing powdered B_2O_3 with magnesium, but in 1940–1943 Laubengayer, Hurd, Newkirk, and Hoard succeeded in making pure crystalline boron and determining its structure. They reduced boron trichloride with hydrogen on a hot metallic filament, and obtained black, hard, shiny crystals of density* 2.33. These crystals have a complicated structure, with a tetragonal unit cell containing fifty atoms. The boron atoms are closely bound in interconnected polyhedra with a spacing of 1.89Å, and this is why the crystals are so hard and strong. Among the elementary substances, only diamond exceeds boron in these respects, and even then not by much.

Despite its unmetallic appearance, boron is an electronic semiconductor even at room temperature; diamond is not. The difficulty of obtaining single crystals of a substance which melts at 2300°C, plus the difficulty of introducing and retaining controlled amounts of impurity for electrical purposes, would seem to preclude the possibility of making ordinary transistors or rectifiers of boron, but the element is of some value as a high-temperature deoxidizer for aluminum and for alloy steels, and as a neutron absorber in nuclear reactors. We shall be concerned less with the element than with certain compounds of boron, all of which are unusual or peculiar enough to be memorable.

THE HARD FACTS

"Hardness" is a common and familiar enough property, and yet one of the most difficult to measure. The metallurgist measures it by forcing a diamond point into the metal under known force and then measuring the depth of the impression. The mineralogist measures it by scratch tests, a tricky procedure which gives only relative results, of course, but is suitable for brittle substances. In the mineralogists' scale of hardness (the Moh scale), diamond stands at the top with a score of 10, corundum or sapphire at 9, topaz at 8, quartz at 7, and so on. Every petrographer knows that there is more space between 9 and 10 on this scale than between 1 and 9, and that it is very difficult to rate extremely hard materials.** Nevertheless, people try, and they

---

* As used herein, *density* is always given in grams per cubic centimeter.

** Even the different forms of diamond, which have minor crystallographic differences, exhibit different scratch hardness. Which form is 10?

try also to relate scratch hardness to various mechanical measurements that show some relation, and so we may have some confidence in the figures. It develops that crystalline boron has a hardness of 9.30, while boron carbide stands at 9.32 (compare silicon carbide at 9.15), and cubic, diamond-structure boron nitride at 9.8.

In order to understand the reasons for this array of very hard boron-containing substances, we must look to their structure. The structures of three different kinds of crystalline boron and of many of its compounds have been worked out by x-ray diffraction,* and here the individuality of boron comes to light at once. The structures are very peculiar. The three forms of elementary boron are all made up of tightly-bound little icosahedra,** one of which is shown in Fig. 4.1. In the best-known form of boron, which is stable at ordinary temperatures, these icosahedra are close-packed in a nearly cubic structure. Within the icosahedra the B-B distance is 1.76Å, but between the icosahedra there are two types of bond, one with a distance of 1.71Å and one which is a three-center bond with a distance of 2.03Å.

Figure 4.1 The icosahedron, structural unit in elementary boron, boron carbide, and certain boron hydrides.

We must take time at this point to consider what is meant by a three-center bond. In the ordinary familiar two-center covalent bond, two atomic orbitals overlap and interact to form one bonding (molecular) orbital and one antibonding (molecular) orbital. If only two

* See A. F. Wells, *Structural Inorganic Chemistry*, 3rd ed., p. 819, Oxford Univ. Press, 1962, for a general summary; and W. N. Lipscomb, *Boron Hydrides*, W. A. Benjamin, New York, 1963, for a discussion of the hydrides.

** From Pythagoras onward, mathematicians have shown that only five regular solids are possible, and the icosahedron is one of them. It has 20 equilateral triangles for faces, and these meet at 12 corners, where the boron atoms may be considered to be placed in the drawing of Fig. 4.1.

electrons are available (one from each atom, or two from one atom and none from the other), these go into the bonding orbital, and the two partner atoms are held together. (The antibonding orbital stands at a higher potential energy, and so is not filled unless there are more electrons than the bonding orbital can accommodate; if it *is* filled, then there is no net bonding effect because the bonding and anti-bonding forces cancel each other.) In a *three-center* bond, three atomic orbitals overlap as shown in Fig. 4.2 and interact to produce one bonding (molecular) orbital and several antibonding orbitals.

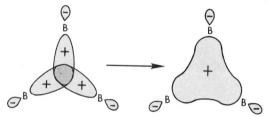

Figure 4.2 Overlap of three orbitals to form a three-center covalent bond between boron atoms.

(The plus signs indicate the bonding orbital, or more strictly, the sign of the wave function.) If there are only enough electrons to fill the bonding orbital, the three atoms are held together by the resulting covalent bond.* It follows that three-center bonds are particularly convenient and appropriate for atoms which have too few electrons to "complete their octets" by forming ordinary two-center covalent bonds and at the same time are not sufficiently electropositive to act like a metal and engage in metallic bonding. Such a statement de-scribes the element boron perfectly, and boron's unique position as the smallest atom with a chronic electron deficiency makes it a natural candidate for the greatest use of three-center bonding.** In fact, boron stands quite alone in this respect.

Returning to the exceedingly hard black crystals of elementary boron, at temperatures above 1500°C a more complex rhombohedral arrangement is produced, with 108 atoms in the unit cell. A third

---

* If there were enough electrons available to fill all the antibonding orbitals too, the atoms would fly apart because the antibonding orbitals have a repelling effect.

** Small size makes for greater attraction for the pair of electrons being shared by the atoms, and hence a stronger three-center bond than a larger atom could form.

43

form, with 50 atoms in the unit cell, is that which is laid down by the hydrogen reduction of BCl_3 on a hot filament, as previously described. Forty-eight of the 50 boron atoms reside in a group of four icosahedra like that of Fig. 4.1, and these are linked together directly and also through the remaining two boron atoms of the unit cell (which atoms have tetragonal symmetry). The spacings are only 1.81 and 1.68Å, and this close multiple bonding makes it easy to understand why boron itself comes so near to diamond in hardness. Diamond has the advantage of a more uniform structure, with its atoms slightly smaller than those of boron and arranged in one giant molecule with a uniform spacing of 1.54Å.

Boron carbide is another very hard substance, and one which is sold in some quantity for use as an abrasive. It is made commercially by reducing B_2O_3 with excess carbon in an electric furnace, at 2500°C, yielding lustrous, black, hard crystals. The structure of these crystals is most peculiar. The boron atoms are all clustered in the familiar B_{12} icosahedra, as in Fig. 4.1, and these are connected by linear chains of carbon atoms, each chain containing 3 carbons. The result is a repetitive unit of B_{12} and C_3, leading to an empirical formula of B_4C (a composition which was known long before the structure was determined). Objects of massive boron carbide have been produced for grinding mortars and the like, and minute crystals of boron carbide are precipitated within certain molybdenum and tungsten alloys which are valued as hard, tough, refractory metals for use at very high temperatures.

Boron nitride is very different from the element and the carbide. As is best illustrated by a Lewis dot diagram, a boron-nitrogen bond is isoelectronic with a carbon-carbon bond

$$\cdot \overset{\cdot\;\cdot}{\underset{\cdot}{B}} : \overset{}{\underset{\cdot}{N}} \cdot \qquad \text{vs.} \qquad \cdot \overset{\cdot\;\cdot}{\underset{\cdot\;\cdot}{C}} : \overset{}{C} \cdot$$

three electrons coming from the boron atom and five from the nitrogen atom vs. four electrons from each of two carbon atoms. Since the boron and nitrogen atoms are nearly the same size as a carbon atom, it follows that B-N pairs should fit into familiar carbon structures. The most striking proof of this hypothesis is the ordinary form of boron nitride itself: it is a slippery white powder with the crystal structure of graphite, but without the electrical conductivity and opacity of graphite. Its atoms are arranged in flat layers with a neat hexagonal pattern, the B-N distance being only 1.44Å, and these

44

layers or sheets are separated from each other by a spacing of 3.38Å. Boron nitride is very stable and refractory; it melts at 3000°C under pressure, and is not affected much by oxygen or oxidizing agents. In this last respect it is superior to graphite, and so chemists were led to wonder whether a cubic form of boron nitride, as yet unknown, would not be superior to diamond in oxidation resistance, and yet be just as hard. An opportunity to find out came after high-pressure, high-temperature techniques had been worked out for converting graphite to diamond.* Ordinary layer-structure boron nitride, with a density of 2.20, was subjected to the same conditions of high pressure and high temperature, and came out with the dense diamond structure! The substance is now made commercially under the name of *borazon*; it has a hardness very close to that of diamond, although still inferior, and it resists oxidation so well that it is preferred to diamond in high-speed tools that get very hot. It also breaks with sharper cutting edges, and so is superior to diamond as an abrasive.

This adaptability of boron-nitrogen compounds to carbonaceous structures extends still further into carbon chemistry, producing what might be called pseudo-organic compounds. The best known example (but not the only one**) is borazole, $B_3N_3H_6$, which has a structure very much like that of benzene, C_6H_6. Table 4.1 gives the interatomic distances of the two hexagonal molecules and lists some of their properties. The similarity is remarkable, but at the same time there are some marked differences. Borazole has two different hydrogen distances, and so the ring is not absolutely planar in the sense that benzene is. Furthermore, borazole does not have the chemical behavior of an aromatic hydrocarbon. As for stability and reactivity, borazole has high thermal stability (only 27% is decomposed after 30 min. at 500°C), but hydrolyses slowly in acid solutions.

THE QUEER HYDRIDES

All the natural boron-containing minerals are fully oxidized, as would be expected from the principles outlined in Chapter 3. Never-

---

* Wentorf, Hall, Nerad, and others, General Electric Co., 1955.

** See Table 17.13, p. 799, of T. Moeller, *Inorganic Chemistry*, Wiley, New York, 1952, for a list of 18 B-N compounds vs. their organic analogs, with physical properties for both.

Table 4.1

Some Properties of Borazole vs. Benzene

	$B_3N_3H_6$	C_6H_6
B-N distance, Å	1.44	—
N-H distance, Å	1.02	—
B-H distance, Å	1.20	—
C-C distance, Å	—	1.39
C-H distance, Å	—	1.08
MW by vapor density	80.2	78.1
mp, °C	−58	5.5
bp, °C	53	79.6
density at mp	0.898	0.890

theless, more than fifty years ago chemists synthesized volatile boron halides and alkoxides. The fact that these substances hydrolysed readily and reverted to boric acid was readily explainable in terms of the affinity of boron for oxygen, and the same reasoning would lead one not to expect natural hydrides of boron. At the same time, this conclusion challenged chemists to make hydrides under conditions that would protect them from air and water, just to see whether they could be made and to find out what they were like.

Alfred Stock, a famous German inorganic chemist noted for his tenacity of purpose, found that when B_2O_3 was reduced by excess magnesium, considerable amounts of magnesium boride were formed, and when the entire reduction mixture was added rapidly to hydrochloric acid, the hydrogen which came off contained small amounts of odorous, reactive gases containing boron. Stock proceeded to devise apparatus and techniques for preparing, distilling, analysing, and conducting reactions with the mysterious gases, and in the period 1910 to 1930 he (and a long succession of junior collaborators) succeeded in isolating six different hydrides: B_2H_6, B_4H_{10}, B_5H_9, B_5H_{11}, B_6H_{10}, and $B_{10}H_{14}$. The physical properties of these compounds have already been given in Table 3.3, and are not particularly important here. We are more concerned at this time with the unusual bonding that holds together the boron hydrides, and with the evolution of chemical thought that gradually led to useful new theories. It is significant that during the thirty years that the boron hydrides were anomalies, incapable of explanation under existing theories of

46

chemical combination, not a single new hydride of boron was discovered. Later, when molecular orbital theory and the topological concept of structure were evolved, chemists at last had some guiding principles to aid them in their search, and four new substances (B_9H_{15}, $B_{10}H_{16}$, $B_{18}H_{22}$, and iso-$B_{18}H_{22}$) were isolated and identified. In addition, indications of about twenty other hydrides or derivatives of hydrides have been obtained, and the field is expanding rapidly at the time of writing.

The problem which the boron hydrides presented to ordinary valence theory may be outlined very simply. In the first place, the lowest hydride definitely is B_2H_6; Stock tried hard to find a BH_3 corresponding to BF_3, BCl_3, $B(CH_3)_3$, and so on, but he could not. Moreover, whenever he dissociated B_2H_6 he got only the elements and some condensation products, but never any BH_3. This is peculiar; there *are* enough electrons to make a BH_3 with ordinary covalent bonds, if we overlook the "open sextet" on boron for the moment

$$\begin{array}{c} H \\ \cdot\cdot \\ H : B : H \end{array}$$

but there definitely *are not* enough electrons for a B_2H_6 by ordinary standards

$$\begin{array}{c} H \quad H \\ \cdot\cdot \quad \cdot\cdot \\ H : B : B : H \\ \cdot \quad \cdot \\ H \quad H \end{array}$$

We have only three electrons from each of the two boron atoms, and six from the six hydrogen atoms, or a total of 12 electrons, and 14 are needed for the seven covalent bonds of an ethanelike structure. It is unsatisfactory to write single-electron bonds for two of the hydrogen atoms, as shown, and it is not any more suitable to deprive the boron atoms of their bond, because early structural studies showed that the boron atoms were adjacent. What is worse, the B-B distance seemed to conform more to the standards of a *double* bond, which would require two more electrons!

Very careful studies by infrared absorption, electron diffraction, and x-ray diffraction led eventually (after several false conclusions) to the structure shown in Fig. 4.3. Here the boron atoms are seen to be connected by two *"bridge" hydrogen atoms*, forming a flat and almost square arrangement, and the other hydrogen atoms extend outward

47

from the boron atoms in a plane at right angles to that of the square. These outer hydrogen atoms are bonded by ordinary, shared-pair covalent bonds, consuming a total of eight of the twelve available electrons. The bridge hydrogens are each involved in a three-center bond like that encountered in the structure of elementary boron; all three atoms are bonded by a single molecular orbital which contains a pair of electrons. The two three-center bonds thereby account for the remaining four electrons, and an entire electron-deficient molecule can be bonded firmly together by the twelve available electrons.

It cannot be emphasized too strongly that the bridge hydrogens of Fig. 4.3 are *not* divalent in the sense of forming two ordinary covalent bonds, nor indeed in any sense. The lines are put in Fig. 4.3 only to show the geometry of the molecule, not to indicate bonds. In the

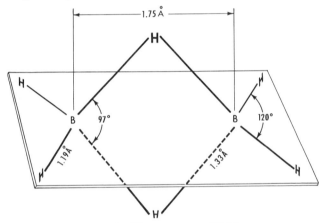

Figure 4.3   The structure of B_2H_6.

three-center bonds the hydrogen atoms are simply participants in the triplex partnership, and are not divalent bridges at all. As is shown in Fig. 4.4, the spherically symmetrical 1s orbital of a hydrogen atom overlaps with two sp^3 hybrid atomic orbitals of the boron atoms, producing one bonding molecular orbital and two antibonding orbitals. Since there are only two electrons available (and these must be of opposite spin), only the bonding orbital is filled, and the result is a force of attraction. It follows that in more complex hydrides there can be B-B-B three-center bonds, or B-H-B three-center bonds, or three-center bonds of both kinds, along with ordinary two-center covalent bonds, all within one molecule. These will be assumed

48

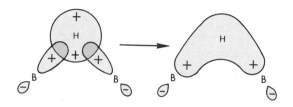

Figure 4.4 Formation of a B—H—B three-center bond.

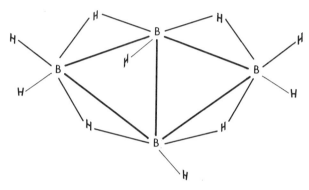

Figure 4.5 Arrangement of atoms in B_4H_{10}. (The figure is not all in one plane.)

from the structures and the electron complement, without further explanation.

The higher hydrides of boron may now be described more briefly. In B_4H_{10} there are four B-H-B three-center bonds, while the other six hydrogen atoms are held by ordinary two-center bonds, as is shown in Fig. 4.5. For the structure of B_5H_9, imagine a square pyramid with boron atoms at the four base corners and the apex (Fig. 4.6), and with one hydrogen atom attached individually to each boron atom. The remaining four hydrogen atoms participate in four B-H-B three-center bonds involving all the base boron atoms. In B_5H_{11} there is a similar arrangement, but without a symmetrical base to the pyramid; the boron atom at the apex and two other boron atoms carry two nonbridge hydrogens each and the other two base boron atoms one hydrogen each; thus, there are only three bridge hydrogens.

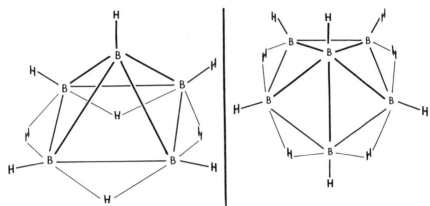

Figure 4.6 Structure of B_5H_9. | *Figure 4.7* Structure of B_6H_{10}.

When we come to B_6H_{10} we begin to see a resemblance to the icosahedron of elementary boron which introduced this chapter. Fig. 4.7 shows the familiar triangular faces and pentagonal body outline of an icosahedron, and indeed we can consider B_6H_{10} to be just half of a B_{12} icosahedron trimmed with appropriate bridge and nonbridge hydrogen atoms. In B_9H_{15} we find a larger fragment of the icosahedron, and in $B_{10}H_{14}$ it looks almost finished except for the roof. In the carboranes, which are carbon-containing derivatives of the boron hydrides, the icosahedron is complete but is made up of ten boron atoms and two carbon atoms, giving a $B_{10}C_2$ framework and leading to the formula $B_{10}C_1H_{12}$. Not all the higher hydrides seem to head for the icosahedral structure, however; $B_{10}H_{16}$ consists rather of two B_5H_9 pyramids joined apex to apex, without any apical hydrogen atoms.

This short look at the boron hydrides shows how special the structural and chemical aspects of boron can be, mostly as a result of its peculiar position as the lightest metalloid. Yet the hydrides are all reactive, volatile substances, especially active toward oxygen, the halogen elements, and bases like ammonia; they stand in sharp contrast to the inert, refractory, hard solids such as borazon and boron carbide. The key to all this lies in the special aptitude of boron for three-center covalent bonding, a story entitled "How to Get the Most Bonding with the Fewest Electrons." From our understanding of this aptitude will come a great deal more new boron chemistry in the next decade, and undoubtedly many applications. A few of these will be surmised in Chapter 8.

CHAPTER **5**

The Best-Known Ones: Silicon and Germanium

We turn now to the metalloids of the Fourth Group, two elements which are not tricky or unusual in their types of chemical combination and which are known to every student of introductory chemistry. In this age of solid-state electronics these two elements probably are the most familiar of the metalloids, at least in the sound of their names. The word "known" is not used in the sense of "understood," however, because we actually know and understand very little about the chemical behavior of germanium (a neglected element, it has been called). For that matter, there are many aspects of the chemistry of silicon that need clearing up.

Students are taught to associate the names of silicon and germanium, for in Mendeleef's day the hypothetical germanium was known as eka-silicon. Fourteen years after Mendeleef's prediction, in 1886, Winkler discovered the element in argyrodite (a sulfide of silver) and named it after his own country. Much has been made of the precise prediction of properties and chemical behavior of germanium by Mendeleef, and of the close correspondence with the actual facts discovered later on, but a more critical look at the comparison shows that only the physical constants were predicted with precision, not the chemical behavior. This is not to detract from Mendeleef's triumph, for it is all the more remarkable that with the information available to him 95 years ago Mendeleef was able to interpolate so exactly the density of the element (5.5, vs. 5.36 found), the density of the oxide (4.7, vs. 4.703 found), the density of the tetra-chloride (1.9 at 0°, vs. 1.88 at 20° found), and its boiling point ("under 100°," vs. 86.5° found). Interpolation of the properties of an unknown

51

element from those of its neighbors was indeed established by Mendeleef as a powerful tool. But notice also that Mendeleef predicted that elementary eka-silicon would "decompose steam with difficulty," whereas germanium actually does not decompose it at all. This is to say that germanium is less metallic than was predicted. Mendeleef also said that acids would have a slight action on the element, but they do not have any action on germanium; again, it is a more negative element than was predicted. There are many more chemical facts which point in the same direction: the conclusion is simply that germanium is more electronegative than was expected by interpolation, and it actually behaves a great deal like arsenic.

Silicon and germanium differ a great deal more in another respect, and that is in abundance: silicon is present on earth to the extent of 277,200 parts per million, while germanium is present only in 7 parts per million. This sharp difference apparently has to do with the nuclear structures of the two elements; silicon's 14 protons and 14 neutrons correspond to filled energy levels, while germanium's 32 protons and 42 neutrons (in the principal isotope) do not.* In the genesis of the elements, the stable and unreactive $^{28}_{14}$Si nuclear structure has persisted.

There are plenty of books about silicon, and some parts of books about germanium, as the reader will find in Chapter 9, therefore no extensive survey is planned here. Instead, only a few topics will be pursued, and these with a somewhat different emphasis than is current in textbooks.

ELEMENTARY SILICON FOR DIFFERENT PURPOSES

Since there is no practical limitation on the amount of silicon available, and we have plenty of concentrated sources of it, and since it has a varied but reliable chemical behavior, we might expect that silicon would be a favorite chemical raw material for industry. In practice, this potential has not been widely realized except in the building industry and in the ceramic arts, which have had the advantage of ten thousand years of development. The entry of silicon and its compounds into the manufacture of plastics, fibers, elastomers, coatings, and even cosmetics has been slow; natural products have

---

* See the Mayer scheme of quantized nuclear energy levels in Friedlander and Kennedy, *Nuclear and Radio Chemistry*, Wiley, New York, 1955.

sufficed so far for clothing and furniture and finishes, and so there has not been much incentive to create something new and unnatural. Nevertheless, there are a few large-scale applications which require elementary silicon as a starting material, and we should consider how the material is obtained.

At ordinary temperatures the free energy change is adverse for obtaining silicon from its oxide by reduction with carbon, and indeed the same can be said for magnesium. Instead, the reverse reaction is common: magnesium burns fiercely in an atmosphere of carbon dioxide, or even mixed with powdered Dry Ice, and silicon also will take the oxygen away from carbon dioxide at 1200°C. At much higher temperatures the situation is reversed, and so at 3000°C or so there can be carbothermic reduction of both silicon and magnesium oxides. To attain so high an operating temperature, an electric current of thousands of amperes is passed through a mass of coke and oxide, heating it by means of its own resistance. In the present instance, a charge of selected silica sand and crushed coke is heated in such a resistance furnace, out of contact with air, and liquid silicon (mp 1420°C) collects at the bottom of the furnace. Volatile silicon monoxide distils off, a by-product without much use, and some silicon carbide also forms even though the Si/C ratio is carefully controlled. Since iron and aluminum oxides inevitably are present in the silica sand, these elements also appear in the reduction product, along with some calcium, titanium, and a few other metals. However, massive silicon "metal" containing only one percent or so of iron and half a percent of aluminum (with less than a tenth of a percent each of calcium, titanium, and other metals) can be produced commercially, and is available by the thousands of tons. Other grades are made with increasing proportions of iron present (ferrosilicons), these being lower melting and more convenient to use in the steel industry.

The principal uses of 98% silicon and the various grades of ferrosilicon are metallurgical. Silicon is a precipitation-hardening constituent of aluminum aircraft alloys, being slightly soluble in hot melted aluminum but forced out of solution in microscopic crystals during later heat treatment. Silicon also is a deoxidizer for alloy steels and for some nonferrous metals. A cast silicon-iron containing 14% Si is brittle but is highly resistant to acids and to most other chemical reagents; it is used for laboratory drains and industrial conduits. A thin-rolled silicon steel (in which several percent of silicon greatly increases the electrical resistance) is very important to all electrical

machinery designed for alternating-current operation; every transformer and AC motor has a laminated magnetic core made up of such sheets, each insulated from its neighbor, in order to reduce the circulation of eddy currents induced in the core by changing magnetic flux. And lastly, 98% silicon is a raw material for making silicone polymers and for making the hyperpure silicon needed for transistors, rectifiers, and solar batteries.

Hyperpure silicon requires many stages in its manufacture, as was indicated in Chapter 2. Silicon tetrachloride or trichlorosilane, $SiHCl_3$ (both derived from chlorination reactions of silicon or ferrosilicon) is fractionally distilled at great length to free it from BCl_3, $AsCl_3$, etc., and then is reduced by pure magnesium or zinc. The metal chloride is sublimed off, and the silicon may be purified further by converting it to the tetraiodide and then dissociating the iodide thermally. The last steps are to fuse the silicon and grow single crystals which can be subjected to zone refining. These steps are so elaborate and exacting that the silicon which began as ordinary sand ends up worth several hundred dollars per pound. (See Fig. 5.0.)

THE SILICATES

The term *silicates* includes both the organic esters of silicic acid, which are made by the action of alcohols or phenols on silicon tetrachloride, and the inorganic silicates, which may be considered as salts of the various silicic acids. We shall concentrate on a short summary of the ionic silicates, and, since the supposed parent silicic acids are largely hypothetical, we shall consider these inorganic silicates purely from the structural and morphological point of view. The scope of the subject can only be described as vast, so that in a book of this size only the essentials can be presented. The importance of the inorganic silicates is enormous, too; they make up most of the solid earth we stand on and the moon and planets we hope to reach. They have been the raw materials for pottery and earthenware since the stone age days, and they are the basis of today's manufacture of cement, bricks, tile, glass, and vitreous enamel.

We may as well begin by expecting every conceivable structure based on tetrahedral silicon atoms and divalent oxygen atoms. The word "divalent" is used with special emphasis, because oxygen atoms are *never* doubly bonded to silicon atoms with sigma and *p*-pi bonds the way they are bonded to carbon in the carbonyl group or in carbon

54

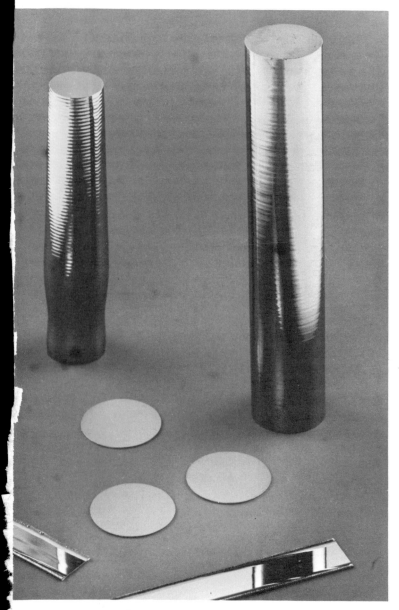

Figure 5.0 Single-crystal silicon grown specifically for epitaxy substrate and solar cell blanks, by Dow Corning's Electronic Products Division.

monoxide. The oxygen atoms in silicates either are bonded to different silicon atoms, or are bonded to one and are left with a s negative charge:

Combination of these two forms of oxygen, in company with th required number of silicon atoms, gives rise to all the silicate negative ions. Thus a single silicon atom with four oxygen atoms of the second type corresponds to the orthosilicate ion, SiO_4^{4-}:

The tetrasodium salt of this ion, sodium orthosilicate, Na_4SiO_4, is a very soluble constituent of one form of water glass, but the mixe magnesium and iron orthosilicate, called olivine, $(Mg, Fe)_2SiO_4$,* a very common and highly insoluble mineral. The orthosilicate Be_2SiO_4 (phenacite), $ZrSiO_4$ (zircon), and Zn_2SiO_4 (willemite) als are good examples from the store of natural minerals.

If two silicate tetrahedra share one oxygen atom we are left with only six negative charges on the Si_2O_7 structure:

Similarly, there may be combinations of three or four tetrahedra, giving rise to Si_3O_{10} and Si_4O_{13} ions with eight and ten negative charges, respectively. Since there is no limitation as to size or length in actual silicates, the chains of alternate silicon and oxygen atoms may be indefinitely long, and so may constitute a truly polymeric

---

* The formula $(Mg, Fe)_2SiO_4$ means that the mineral olivine, although it is a single phase, contains variable proportions of magnesium and iron. The Mg^{2+} and Fe^{2+} ions are nearly the same size, and can replace each other in the crystal lattice.

negative ion (a "polyanion"). The repeated unit is an SiO_3 chain segment

$$\left[\begin{array}{c} O \\ | \\ Si \\ \diagup \, | \, \diagdown \\ O \quad O- \end{array} \right]^{2-}$$

called a metasilicate unit. This segment carries two negative charges, so that two positive charges can be bound by each such structural unit. An example is the mineral diopside, $(MgCa(SiO_3)_2)_x$, related to the amphibole minerals. Iron is a common substituent for the magnesium.

There is no structural reason why extension of the silicate chains need be limited to one dimension, so we may expect cross-linking of the metasilicate chains. Complete local cross-linking gives the neat hexagonal pattern of Fig. 5.1, which is the negative-ion structure of the asbestos variety of amphibole. The long strings of siloxane hexagons show clearly why asbestos cleaves in long fibers, and why these fibers show marked flexibility. Alert readers also will recognize that if the bond angles for silicon and oxygen are favorable for the formation of hexagonal structures such as the chain segments of Fig. 5.1, isolated hexagons surrounded by singly-bonded, negatively-charged oxygen atoms should also be possible. The discrete Si_6O_{18} ion, with its concomitant twelve negative charges, is such a ring structure, with six silicon atoms alternating with six oxygen atoms in the ring. This is the structural unit of beryl, $Be_3Al_2Si_6O_{18}$, perhaps

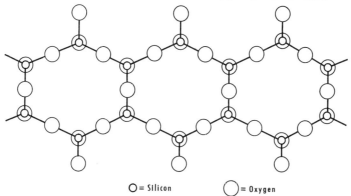

O = Silicon   ⬡ = Oxygen

Figure 5.1 Top view of the molecular structure of the silicate mineral amphibole asbestos.

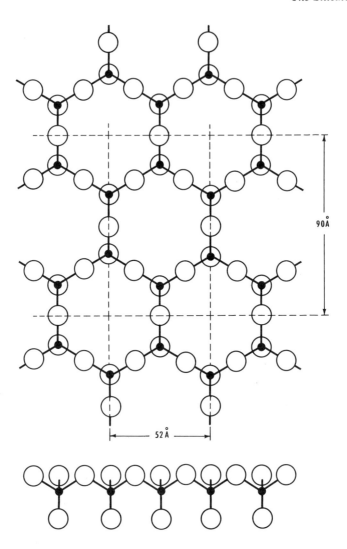

Figure 5.2 Diagram of the silicate structure in the formation of siloxane sheets in silicate minerals. (Reproduced by permission from H. J. Emeleus and J. S. Anderson, *Modern Aspects of Inorganic Chemistry*, 2nd ed., Van Nostrand, New York, 1954.)

better known to most readers as aquamarine if it is a pale transparent blue, and as emerald if it is a deep green in color. The crystals are

hexagonal, reflecting the ionic structure, and it has been pointed out*
that the layers of hexagons are so disposed as to leave open channels
down their centers, spaces large enough to accommodate small gas
molecules.

It is but a small step in structural thinking from the infinite chains
of Fig. 5.1 to two-dimensional networks or sheets of hexagons such
as is shown in Fig. 5.2. These layers of silicon and oxygen atoms are
the distinguishing characteristic of the layer minerals (mica and talc,
for example), where the sheets are about 20Å apart and are held
together by coordination to magnesium ions. In other layer structures,
such as those of the clay minerals kaolinite and halloysite, aluminum
atoms replace some of the silicon atoms, with corresponding reduction
in the number of negative charges on the entire polyanion.

A final extension of the principle of cross-linking of siloxane chains
occurs when we consider extension of the chains in *three* dimensions.
The several crystalline forms of pure silicon dioxide best illustrate this
structure; Fig. 5.3 shows a part of the arrangement in β-quartz. The
entire crystal is one large molecule composed of interlocked siloxane
chains, of which only two are shown in the diagram. Because of the
bond angles of silicon and oxygen, each chain has a spiral configuration as it extends throughout the crystal. Each silicon atom is a cross-

Figure 5.3 A portion of the structure of β-Quartz.

* H. J. Emeléus and J. S. Anderson, *Modern Aspects of Inorganic Chemistry*,
2nd ed., p. 239, Van Nostrand, New York, 1954. The entire Chapter VII is an
excellent reference on silicates.

ing-point for two such spiral chains, so that the chains extend in three dimensions. The result is to tie the entire structure together into a completely cross-linked polymer of high melting point (1470°C) and considerable hardness (7). This is in sharp contrast to carbon dioxide, which is monomeric and gaseous as a result of the specific attachment of oxygen to carbon through combined sigma and pi bonds (the classical double bonds of organic chemistry).

The few structural types which have been reviewed here embrace hundreds of silicate minerals, but by no means all of them. There are many structures which are far more complicated than have been indicated here. Furthermore, polymorphism is very common among the silicate minerals, greatly increasing the number of phases involved. Consider, for example, the α and β forms of quartz, tridymite, and crystobalite, all six phases representing only pure SiO_2. If we add vitreous SiO_2 (in which the regularity of structure is much the same, but of shorter order) and the many hydrated and amorphous forms of SiO_2 (such as opal, chalcedony, agate, and flint), we get some idea of the complexity of the subject.

As a final warning, one should not expect that silicate minerals always have an external appearance that reflects their internal structure. That can be so, of course, especially if well-formed crystals are laid down from solution or from a melt. Sometimes, however, the actual morphology is determined by microorganisms, or by metamorphic processes, and the result seems to have nothing to do with the interior structure. Thus a survey of clay minerals by electron micrography* shows some in accordion-pleated ribbons, some in twisted rods and fibers, some in amazingly intricate skeletons of tiny animals long since gone, and some even in the form of minute hollow tubes like soda straws. The properties and uses of such clay minerals often depend upon the peculiar morphology of the substance rather than on its composition or its crystal structure.

GLASS AND CERAMICS

The term *glass* represents a state of matter and not a chemical composition, and some glasses (borate and phosphate glasses, for example) may contain no silicon at all. Other perfectly good glasses

---

* *Reference Clay Minerals*, American Petroleum Institute Research Project No. 49, by P. F. Kerr and others (Columbia Univ., N. Y., 1951).

may be based on germanium dioxide instead of silica. Usually, however, the word *glass* refers to a silicate glass, which is a supercooled liquid solution of metal oxides in acidic SiO_2, with possible additions of B_2O_3 or Al_2O_3 as well. Similarly, the term *ceramic* refers not only to fired objects made of clay, but also to all compositions and objects made of oxides or minerals and fired in a similar way. Thus there can be ceramic parts made of pure sintered Al_2O_3, or of MgO, or of ThO_2 or BeO. Nevertheless, we shall consider only silicate compositions here.

Those glasses which are produced in large quantity are made by fusing together silica sand, limestone, sodium carbonate or sulfate, borax, and potassium carbonate in an enormous rectangular "tank" lined with sintered blocks of fused alumina. The "tank" is really a reverberatory furnace, covered with a curved roof under which gas flames are directed. Molten silicates are good solvents for firebrick and all ordinary refractories, but dense alumina blocks dissolve more slowly than any other kind of material and so are worth their considerable expense as a lining for the furnace. Once fired up to operating temperature, the furnace is kept going continuously for as many weeks or months as its lining lasts. Raw materials are fed continuously at one end of the "tank," and molten glass is drawn continuously from under the surface of the melt at the other end. The gases which come off from the carbonates and hydrates during the reactions perform the important function of stirring the viscous mass, eventually producing a uniform liquid. Some of the reactions which are involved in the furnace are

$$CaCO_3 \rightarrow CaO + CO_2$$
$$CaO + SiO_2 \rightarrow CaSiO_3$$
$$Na_2CO_3 + SiO_2 \rightarrow Na_2SiO_3 + CO_2$$
$$Na_2SO_4 + SiO_2 \rightarrow Na_2SiO_3 + SO_3$$
$$Na_2B_4O_7 \cdot 12\,H_2O \rightarrow 2\,NaBO_2 + B_2O_3 + 12\,H_2O$$
$$CaO + B_2O_3 \rightarrow Ca(BO_2)_2$$

Glass compositions usually are expressed in terms of parts by weight of the various *oxides* relative to 100 parts of SiO_2. In these terms ordinary window glass usually contains 10.5 parts of CaO, 12.5 parts of Na_2O, 3.8 parts of K_2O, and about 0.3 (accidental) parts of Al_2O_3 per 100 parts of SiO_2. The use of both sodium and potassium oxides extends the working range of the glass; potassium silicates have higher melting points than sodium silicates, and a combination of the two keeps the glass from becoming too fluid or too viscous over the range of temperatures required by the fabricating machinery. Window glass is drawn continuously in a wide, flat ribbon from the red-hot viscous mass. Bottles may be blown from the same kind of glass, using automatic machinery which clips off chunks of liquid glass from the outpouring stream and blows the plastic glass against the confining walls of molds moved along by a conveyer. Lamp bulbs for incandescent lamps are blown in much the same way, but fluorescent lamps are made from tubing drawn continuously from the tank of hot glass; the size of the tubing is controlled by the rate of drawing, and air is blown into the interior of the tube to prevent collapsing of the walls while they are still plastic. The continuous tube is cut in standard lengths as it emerges.

Plate glass formerly was made by casting flat, thick sheets of glass on cast-iron tables, and then grinding and polishing the surfaces to make them flat and smooth. More recently the "float" process has come into use, making unnecessary the elaborate and expensive grinding and polishing operations. In the "float" process the molten glass is poured onto a bed of pure molten tin, which is, of course, perfectly smooth. Because of its much lower density, the liquid glass floats in the molten tin, but does not react with it. As the glass hardens, the surface in contact with the molten tin remains smooth and flat. The upper surface of the glass also is smooth, since it lies quietly while the glass is liquid and touches nothing but still air as it hardens. The hardened sheets are pulled off the tin, cooled further, and cut to size. The system is used widely in England, and is being installed in some plants in the United States.

Laboratory glassware is machine blown, too, but from a different kind of glass. In order to decrease the coefficient of thermal expansion of the glass, thereby making it withstand heat shock better, 12.6 parts of B_2O_3 are added per 100 parts of SiO_2. Since B_2O_3 increases the fluidity, only 4.6 parts of Na_2O and 0.5 parts of K_2O are necessary, and no lime at all. Boric oxide also makes the glass more soluble in alkalies, so to improve the chemical resistance 1.5 parts of Al_2O_3 are added. The result is a high-melting but durable glass.

Porcelain differs from glass in being much higher in alumina, and hence much higher in chemical resistance. The high proportion of aluminum oxide cannot all be dissolved in the silicate matrix, of course; there are myriad tiny crystals held together by a glassy phase of sodium calcium aluminum silicate. Since porcelain is a hetero-

62

geneous material, its strength is not as sensitive to small scratches as is that of a glass; a minute scratch or crack in glass can propagate itself readily through the isotropic material, as when a piece of glass tubing is cut in the laboratory just by scratching and bending it, but a porcelain tube is much harder to break. Besides this greater mechanical strength and chemical inertness, porcelain ware is less sensitive to thermal shock than ordinary glassware. There is also a sharp technological difference: porcelain articles are always shaped cold, from water-softened mixtures of clay and feldspar and other minerals, and then are fired to vitrify them and give them strength, but glass articles are shaped hot by blowing or pressing or drawing the red-hot fluid glass. In this sense glass is the original thermoplastic polymer and is fabricated like all heat-softened plastics, whereas porcelain is pressed cold or shaped on a potter's wheel and then dried and fired.

Earthenware differs from porcelain in being fired at a lower temperature, and hence is weaker and more porous. As water evaporates from the plastic clay used to make earthenware it leaves pores and voids in the solid, and if the dried piece then is fired just enough to cement the particles of clay together with fused silicate, the piece will remain quite porous to air and water. This porosity may be advantageous, as in the Mexican water coolers; if porosity is undesirable, as in pottery tableware, the piece is given a surface glaze by coating it with a suspension of glass particles (or even of ordinary salt) and firing it until a lower-melting glassy skin forms on the surface. Expensive dinnerware is decorated before applying the glaze, and may also be given the final firing at so high a temperature as to bring about a high degree of vitrification, producing a translucent piece of high density.

Brick and tile are more in the realm of primitive earthenware, being porous masses of sintered clay containing considerable iron oxide. Portland cement is still another ceramic product, made by firing a mass of limestone, dolomite and clay in a rotary kiln until it sinters to a clinker. The cooled solid then is ground to a very fine powder. Being rich in calcium, magnesium, and aluminum oxides, the powder absorbs a great deal of water in the process of forming crystalline hydrates, and the interlaced mass of acicular crystals forms a hard, strong body. Since the hydration process is exothermic, heat must be abstracted from a large mass of concrete during the week or so in which the slow hydration and crystallization processes take place.

A mass of hydrated Portland cement by itself would be unnecessarily expensive and undesirably homogeneous; a much stronger and cheaper mass (concrete) is made by mixing sand and crushed rock of varying size with the cement. This is in keeping with the greater durability of heterogeneous materials over homogeneous ones, as explained in connection with glass and porcelain. The sand and stone in concrete are as necessary in a functional way as the glass fiber of reinforced plastic, or the particles of filler in rubber, or the pigment in paint, or the particles of carbide in a fine steel, or the fibers in leather or wood.*

It has been pointed out that the two great and ancient arts upon which the science of chemistry is founded are metallurgy and ceramics. Any student of chemistry will enrich his background and improve his understanding by reading the history of these two arts and by studying the examples around him every day. Some suggestions for reading are given in Chapter 9.

SILICONES

Having considered some of the most ancient applications of the chemistry of silicon compounds, we turn now to one of the most recent. The ideas and the chemical principles will sound familiar, but their embodiment has brought into being some new and unique materials.

The chemical and structural advantages of siloxane chains have been made obvious before this: high thermal stability and chemical inertness due to very strong bonds, and a mutual suitability of atomic sizes and bond angles. We also have seen that silicon, like all the other metalloids, is capable of an extensive organometallic chemistry. The idea of the silicone polymers is to combine the stability of a siloxane framework with the popular features of organic plastics, producing a sort of organic-inorganic material that would have the advantages of each. While the practical idea and its exploitation are quite new, the study of organosilicon compounds purely from scientific curiosity has been going on for a century, as we saw in Chapter 3. It has been extremely helpful to have the accumulated knowledge of a century of research available to aid the recent technology, and the producers

---

* In their zeal for pure homogeneous substances, chemists often overlook the practical advantages of a heterogeneous material (vs. a homogeneous or isotropic one) when they apply their inventions, and may find themselves outdone by more practical men.

of silicone polymers were quick to acknowledge this debt.* Through its own subsequent researches, the silicone industry in turn has greatly enriched and expanded the literature of pure science.

The word *silicone* was coined by F. S. Kipping (see previous footnote) to designate organosilicon oxides of the general composition R_2SiO, where R represents any hydrocarbon group. As an organic chemist, Kipping saw in such compounds a formal analogy to the ketones, R_2CO. However, ketones contain the $C=O$ carbonyl group, and so are monomeric just as carbon dioxide is, while silicones contain the —SI—O—siloxane group, with every oxygen atom linked to *two separate* silicon atoms, and so are always polymeric just as silicon dioxide is. Hence silicones have no ketonelike properties at all, but rather are related to silicate minerals or ceramics in their structures and behavior.

From the general formula R_2SiO, which we must now write in the polymeric form $(R_2SiO)_x$, we could expect a tremendous variety of organosiloxanes as the R group is varied throughout the entire gamut of alkyl and aryl radicals. Quite a few of these compositions have been explored, and the result has been to focus interest sharply on methyl and phenyl silicones because they embody the greatest advantage over the common organic polymers in thermal stability and inertness. Of these two kinds, in turn, methyl silicone is by far the most popular and the most singular in its behavior. It has an absolute minimum of carbon and hydrogen, and no carbon-to-carbon bonds at all, therefore it takes greatest advantage of its inorganic siloxane backbone. Moreover, its physical properties stand in greatest contrast to those of organic materials. For these reasons we shall limit the discussion just to methyl silicone polymers.

The empirical formula of methyl silicone is simply $(CH_3)_2SiO$, and its synthesis is almost as simple as its composition. The methyl groups come from methanol, which is made from coal and water, or from natural gas and air. The silicon comes from 98% metallurgical silicon, manufactured as described at the beginning of this chapter. The oxygen comes from water. The only additional reagent required

---

* The man who did more than any other to advance organosilicon chemistry was Frederick Stanley Kipping, a professor at Nottingham University in England. During the period 1904 through 1945 Kipping and his students published 43 papers about their researches, and these have become the classics in the field. Good summaries of silicone chemistry are mentioned in Chapter 9, and a short historical survey by Richard Müller, entitled "One Hundred Years of Organosilicon Chemistry," appears in the *Journal of Chemical Education*, Vol. 42, p. 31, 1965.

is hydrogen chloride, which is recycled in the process. The raw materials therefore are sand, coal, and water, with natural gas a possible replacement for the coal. The synthesis can be summarized in these steps:

(1) Silicon is made from sand and coke:

$$SiO_2 + 2\,C \rightarrow Si + 2\,CO$$

(2) Methanol is made from coal and water and converted to methyl chloride:

$$H_2O + \text{red hot coal} \rightarrow CO + H_2$$

$$CO + H_2O \rightarrow CO_2 + H_2$$

$$CO + 2\,H_2(\text{over ZnO} + Cr_2O_3, 350°C, 200\ atm) \rightarrow CH_3OH$$

$$CH_3OH + HCl(ZnCl_2\ \text{catalyst}) \rightarrow CH_3Cl + H_2O$$

(3) Methyl chloride reacts with hot silicon as in Chapter 3:

$$2\,CH_3Cl + Si(\text{Cu catalyst}) \rightarrow (CH_3)_2SiCl_2,$$

with CH_3SiCl_3 and $(CH_3)_3SiCl$ as by-products.

(4) Dimethyldichlorosilane is isolated by distillation and is hydrolysed:

$$4\,(CH_3)_2SiCl_2 + 4\,H_2O \rightarrow [(CH_3)_2SiO]_4 + 8\,HCl$$

(Some linear HO $[(CH_3)_2SiO]_xH$ is produced, too, but this can be converted to octamethylcyclotetrasiloxane, which is the tetramer shown above, by heating with NaOH.)

(5) Pure by-product $(CH_3)_3SiCl$ also is hydrolysed:

$$2\,(CH_3)_3SiCl + H_2O \rightarrow (CH_3)_3Si{-}O{-}Si(CH_3)_3 + 2\,HCl$$

(6) The hydrogen chloride from steps (4) and (5) is returned to step (2).

Having prepared these methyl chlorosilanes and methyl siloxanes as intermediates, the various kinds of methyl silicone polymer can then be made from them by appropriate conversion processes. The simplest conversion to understand is that which makes silicone rubber, a high polymer with a molecular weight in the millions. Very pure octamethylcyclotetrasiloxane, $[(CH_3)_2SiO]_4$, which has been distilled until it contains less than 0.001% of trifunctional or monofunctional siloxane material, is warmed with 0.02% of anhydrous potassium hydroxide, which converts the mobile liquid to a viscous gum:

$[(CH_3)_2SiO]_4 + KOH$
$$\rightarrow HO(CH_3)_2SiO(CH_3)_2SiO(CH_3)_2SiO(CH_3)_2SiOK$$

$$-SiOH + HOSi- \rightarrow H_2O + -Si-O-Si-$$

$$H_2O + -SiOK \rightarrow KOH + -SiOH \text{ etc.}$$

The process goes on, regenerating potassium hydroxide and condensing the siloxane chains end-to-end until the mass becomes solid. The catalyst then has done its work, and is removed. The resulting gel or gum is mixed with very finely divided silica filler (called a "reinforcing agent") and then is molded or pressed or extruded in the desired shape. The rubber finally is "cured" by heating it with a small amount of oxidizing agent which had previously been mixed in along with the filler. The curing action consists in the oxidation of a few methyl groups at desired intervals along the siloxane chain, resulting in $Si-CH_2-CH_2-Si$ cross links at these points. From then on the silicone rubber is no longer plastic nor sticky, and looks very much like a piece of white or gray natural rubber. It behaves very differently from natural rubber, though, in several respects:

a) Silicone rubber withstands a much higher operating temperature than natural rubber without melting or decomposing or charring. It can be used at temperatures of 700°F for many hours, and at much higher temperatures for short periods (as on the heat shield of a space ship upon re-entry into the atmosphere). Silicone rubber therefore makes good electrical insulation for wires that get hot, and is used also to seal hot-air deicer and heating ducts in airplanes.

b) Silicone rubber also withstands much *lower* operating temperatures than natural rubber. Below zero natural rubber stiffens, and at the temperature of Dry Ice ($-80°C$) it is as brittle as glass (as a common lecture demonstration shows). Methyl silicone rubber is still flexible at $-80°C$, and so can perform its function as an elastic cushion when it is this cold. For this reason silicone rubber is used in jet aircraft to seal the doors and windows, because the operating temperature of such airplanes may go as low as $-60°C$.

67

c) As would be expected from its chemical composition, silicone rubber resists acids very well. It resists bases less successfully, since these will attack the Si—O bonds. Hydrofluoric acid, of course, will dissolve silicone rubber just as it dissolves a silicate glass. Oxygen of the air has little effect on silicone rubber below 300°C, and ozone does not attack it. In most respects, then, silicone rubber is superior to natural rubber in chemical inertness. Its indifference to ozone makes it especially valuable as a high-voltage insulator. It withstands sun and weather well (Fig. 5.4).

Figure 5.4 Silicone rubber (*right*) after 10 years outdoors. Organic rubber (*left*) after 2 years of same exposure.

d) Because of the marked difference in its chemical nature, silicone rubber does not dissolve in hydrocarbon lubricating oil, nor is it softened by such oil. Similarly, chlorinated hydrocarbons (which are disastrous to almost all organic polymers because of their good solvent effect) do not swell or weaken silicone rubber very much. Hence silicone rubber can be used on engine parts exposed to hot lubricating oil, or to chlorinated insulating fluids.

We turn now to silicone oil, which is a methyl silicone polymer of moderate but well-controlled molecular weight. Whereas silicone rubber consists of very long chains of dimethylsiloxane units, presumably with the terminal hydroxyl groups,

$$HOSi(CH_3)_2OSi(CH_3)_2 - - - - - OSi(CH_3)_2OSi(CH_3)_2OH$$

silicone oil has shorter chains which are purposely end-blocked with unreactive trimethylsilyl groups to prevent increase of the molecular weight.

$$(CH_3)_3SiOSi(CH_3)_2O \text{ - - - - - } Si(CH_3)_2OSi(CH_3)_3$$

The end-blocking is accomplished by adding hexamethyldisiloxane to octamethyltetrasiloxane in such proportions as to give the desired ratio of chain-building to chain-terminating groups (thereby determining the average chain length and average molecular weight), and subjecting the solution to a process of "equilibration" with the aid of a tiny amount of 100% H_2SO_4 as catalyst:

$$[(CH_3)_2SiO]_4 + (CH_3)_3SiOSi(CH_3)_3 \xrightarrow{H_2SO_4}$$
$$(CH_3)_3SiOSi(CH_3)_2OSi(CH_3)_2OSi(CH_3)_2OSi(CH_3)_2OSi(CH_3)_3$$

(It will be understood that different proportions of the reagents will give a different chain length from that shown.) The resulting methyl silicone oil is thermally stable, and so it makes a good pump oil for diffusion-type vacuum pumps. It also is a good liquid dielectric or insulator, and a stable cooling fluid. Silicone oil's chief claim to fame, however, is a surprisingly small change of viscosity with temperature; it does not thin out as much at high temperatures as hydrocarbon oils do, nor thicken as much when cold. The viscosity-temperature coefficient, in fact, is only 0.6 vs. 9.0 for a typical automobile lubricating oil. This makes silicone oil a good hydraulic and damping fluid for use over a wide range of temperatures.*

Just as silicone rubber is not affected by hydrocarbon oil, so hydrocarbon rubber is not affected by silicone oil. As a result, silicone oil makes an excellent release agent in the molding of automobile tires; a very thin film of the oil, sprayed on the steel surface of the mold, transfers heat readily but prevents sticking of the rubber to the mold. This is but one of many illustrations of the *abhesive* quality (the failure to stick to anything at all) of methyl silicone polymers. Such abhesiveness is a direct result of the "unnaturalness" or sharply different chemical constitution of methyl silicone; it is unlike the organic polymers, oils, and cements it is likely to come in contact with, and so it is indifferent to them.

A third major type of methyl silicone polymer is silicone resin, a

---

* It is not a good lubricant for automobile engines, however, because it has no chemical attraction for the metal surfaces and so it does not "stay put" under high local pressure.

69

cross-linked thermosetting composition with connected siloxane chains:

$$
\begin{array}{c}
\text{O} \\
| \\
\text{—Si—O—Si—O—Si—O—Si—O—} \\
| \\
\text{O} \\
| \\
\text{—Si—O—Si—O—Si—O—} \\
| \\
\text{O} \\
|
\end{array}
$$

(For clarity, the methyl groups have been left out of the structure.) The more cross-linking of the chains, the more rigid and hard the material becomes (to the point of glasslike brittleness if *every* silicon atom has three oxygen atoms and but one methyl group attached to it). Such resins are condensation products of silanediols and triols, which in turn are hydrolysis products of the corresponding chlorosilanes. Thus the hydrolysis of an equimolar mixture of $(CH_3)_2SiCl_2$ and CH_3SiCl_3, in excess water and with a solvent to dilute the resulting silanols, gives a toluene-soluble mixture which can be kept for a moderate length of time without reacting further. As soon as the solvent is allowed to evaporate, however, and the sticky mass of silanols is heated, the Si—OH groups enter into a condensation reaction, splitting out water and linking everything with Si—O—Si bonds. In our example, a hydrolysed equimolar mixture of bifunctional $(CH_3)_2SiCl_2$ and trifunctional CH_3SiCl_3 eventually would give an insoluble resinous product in which every other silicon atom would be linked to three oxygen atoms (that is, the polymer would be cross-linked at every second silicon atom). Any kind of cross-linking agent could be used, but it is customary to use phenyl trichlorosilane instead of methyl trichlorosilane as a constituent of most silicone resins, in order to increase the resistance to oxidation at high temperatures and to improve the strength of the solid polymer. Hence silicone resins often are methyl phenyl siloxanes in composition, whereas silicone elastomers and oils rarely contain phenyl groups.

As might be expected from the properties of the other silicone polymers, silicone resins are resistant to heat, to oxidation, to chemical agents and to most solvents. These properties make them especially suitable for electrical insulation in heavy-duty motors, generators and transformers. They also can be the bases of heat-resistant enamels and coatings, and as adhesives for glass fibers or mica. Mixed with organic polymers and drying oils, some specially-formulated silicone resins can greatly improve the durability and the life of house paint, or of any outdoor finish.

A few other silicone compositions do not fall within the categories of polymers just considered, yet have important uses. One of these is the "coupling agent" used to obtain a strong bond between organic laminating resins and the glass fibers used to reinforce such resins. The similarity of the siloxane chains in a silicone polymer to the siloxane chains of a silicate glass leads to a strong chemical attraction of silicone resins for glass surfaces, but organic polymers (and especially hydrocarbon resins) do not wet glass fibers nor adhere to them very well. In order to use inexpensive organic resins in combination with glass fibers, a special silicone composition is first applied to the glass, to which it adheres very well. The silicone coating contains unsaturated organic groups which are capable of copolymerizing with an organic monomer such as styrene or methyl methacrylate or butadiene, and so the *in situ* polymerization of the monomer results in a strong coupling of the resulting polymer to the glass base through the silicone coating. The widespread use of glass fiber-reinforced resins would be entirely impractical and unsuccessful if it were not for the silicone coupling agents.

Other methyl silicone compositions markedly depress the foaming of organic oils and varnishes, probably by concentrating on the surface and reducing the surface tension of the oil. In very small amounts, silicone oil controls the bubble size of polyurethane foams without collapsing the foam entirely, leading to a more uniform structure. Still other methyl silicones render the surfaces of cloth, paper, and even stone and brick highly water-repellent, so that they do not soak up or transmit liquid water even though they remain porous to air and to water vapor. Sometimes these silicone compositions are applied from solution, but in other instances they are formed directly on the surface to be treated, as by reaction of a chlorosilane mixture with the surface adsorbed film of water which is present. The formation of a silicone film exactly where it is wanted, and in the desired thickness or thinness, using organochlorosilanes themselves without any preliminary processing, represents the most economical utilization of silicones.

This brief survey indicates some of the ways in which silicones bridge the gap in properties between organic and inorganic materials.

71

We also have seen that there often is need for a material which is *not* like the usual organic or natural products but is radically different in its properties, and that silicone polymers fill this need. Silicones are potentially inexpensive, being based only on sand and coal; it is likely that they will become very common some day. Probably they also will make contributions to the theory of polymer behavior,* and to the techniques of scientific research in many areas. When this comes about, the reader will have had advance knowledge about this new field of chemistry.

---

* See, for example, the relation of the abnormal physical properties of silicone polymers to the intramolecular motions of the constituents, reported in *J. Inorganic and Nuclear Chem.*, Vol. 1, p. 92, 1955.

CHAPTER **6**

Arsenic, Antimony, and Chemotherapy

In a word-association game, almost any player who is accosted with the word "arsenic" will answer "poison!" This particular aspect of arsenic is very much in the public consciousness because "arsenic" (actually the odorless, tasteless, and soluble oxide As_4O_6) seems to have been regarded as a universal poison by the authors of detective stories, and undoubtedly was a favorite instrument of crime in the days of Catherine de Medici and the Borgias. It is very true that arsenic and all its compounds are poisonous, in sufficient doses, and that much needless and unintentional tragedy has been caused in years gone by through the indiscriminate use of arsenic-containing pigments in wallpaper and paints before the hazards were understood. Arsenic is (and always will be) poisonous to the human system, but it is even more poisonous to insects, weeds, and microorganisms, and so it can serve a useful function. As we shall see, it also played an honorable and all-important part in the invention of chemotherapy, which is the art and science of combatting disease by synthesizing chemical agents capable of destroying the cause of the disease. Arsenic also has its nondangerous uses, such as the correction of undesired color in glass and the modification of certain alloys of lead and copper. Together with antimony, its more metallic partner in the fifth group, arsenic deserves some special consideration which it does not get from textbooks.

ARSENIC

No one can be said to have discovered arsenic, because the bright yellow pigment called orpiment (AS_2S_3), a soft, easily-powdered natural mineral, was known to primitive people. They used it and the red realgar (AsS) to decorate their faces and bodies, and to paint earthenware pottery. The name itself comes from the ancient words for orpiment, *arsenikon* in Greek and *az-zernikh* in Arabic.

There is no need to prospect for ores of arsenic today because the various iron, nickel, and cobalt arsenic sulfides occur with the ores of these metals and are a nuisance. Not only is it difficult to keep arsenic out of the metals, but also to keep it out of the sulfuric acid made from by-product sulfur dioxide.* Even coal smoke sometimes contains arsenic trioxide, derived from the $FeAs_2$ which accompanies iron pyrites (FeS_2) in the coal. The volatility of the oxide leads to its being driven off in smelting operations, and so all the arsenic needed for industrial uses can be recovered from the flue dust of copper and lead smelters. The element is easily obtained from the oxide by reducing it with charcoal, but there is little use for the element; the oxide suffices for making the copper and lead arsenates used in plant sprays and for the various chemical applications. The oxide itself sometimes is mixed in garden and lawn topsoil to control weeds and to kill Japanese beetles.

The green pigments which were so popular in the eighteenth and nineteenth centuries were Scheele's green, $CuHAsO_3$, and Paris green, $Cu_2(C_2H_3O_2)AsO_3$. These were made available in large volume by a growing chemical technology, and, before anyone knew better, were used not only in paints and wallpapers, but actually to color confectionery and fancy desserts.** When medical diagnosis was improved to the point of recognizing the symptoms of arsenic poisoning at all its different levels, and particularly after the development

---

* In 1900 the beer-drinkers of Lancashire fell sick by the thousands due to what eventually was diagnosed as chronic arsenic poisoning, and the source of arsenic finally was traced to the sulfuric acid used in refining the sugar used in brewing the beer (see "Some Landmarks in the History of Arsenic Testing," by W. A. Campbell, *Chemistry in Britain*, Vol. 1, p. 198, 1965).

** See article by W. A. Campbell, previous footnote.

of James Marsh's test for arsenic* in 1836 provided a method for testing for minute amounts of the element, a campaign to eliminate all possible sources of arsenic poisoning began. Today there is little danger unless it is deliberate; arsenical pigments are no longer used, and residues from arsenate insecticides are required by law to be kept to extremely low levels on marketed fruit. Once in a while, however, some antique green wallpaper or painted furniture (or even a toy) will be found which contains hazardous amounts of arsenic.

The elementary form of arsenic considered in Chapter 2 was the gamma form, gray (or "metallic") arsenic, with a density of 5.7 and a conductivity of 2.6×10^4 reciprocal ohms per centimeter (about half the conductivity of lead). This is also the most stable form. At 610°C it sublimes to As_4 molecules, analogous to the familiar P_4 molecules. Rapid condensation of the vapor gives yellow (or alpha) arsenic, soluble in carbon disulfide and analogous to white phosphorus but with a density of 2.03. The third form, black, or beta, arsenic, is what forms in the Marsh test and what is obtained when either of the other forms is heated rapidly in a current of hydrogen. Only the gray form is stable over long periods of time; there is even some natural, or native, gray arsenic found in Japan. At 400°C the gray form burns in air with a white flame, and at room temperature (if finely divided) it takes fire in chlorine as it reacts to form $AsCl_3$. Hydrochloric acid does not dissolve gray arsenic, but hot concentrated nitric acid converts it to arsenic acid, H_3AsO_4. The amphoteric nature of arsenic is indicated by the fact that the gray form also dissolves in fused sodium hydroxide, evolving hydrogen and forming sodium arsenite.

Arsenic trichloride, like germanium tetrachloride, hydrolyses reversibly.

$$AsCl_3 + 3 H_2O \rightleftharpoons As(OH)_3 \text{ (or } H_3AsO_3) + 3 HCl$$

The "arsenious acid" which is formed also dissolves in both acids

---

* As most readers know, the Marsh test involves placing a sample of the suspected material in a glass vessel containing some granulated zinc and then adding dilute sulfuric acid. If arsenic is present, arsine (AsH_3) is generated and is evolved along with hydrogen. If the hydrogen is conducted through a slender glass tube heated in a flame, a dark mirror of arsenic deposits on the glass. The deposit of arsenic can be identified by the fact that it is soluble in a solution of sodium hypochlorite, whereas other elements deposited from volatile hydrides are not.

and alkalies. The alkali arsenites are water soluble, although lead and silver arsenites are not.

Arsenic(III) oxide is really As_4O_6 (like P_4O_6), and not As_2O_3. It is soluble in water to about the same extent as the low-temperature form of germanium dioxide, that is, about 2% at 20°C. It sublimes at 193°C, and hence the trouble with its volatility in smelting plants. As for its toxicity, 0.1 gram is usually quoted as a lethal dose, but some individuals can develop a tolerance for this much. The human body always contains some arsenic (usually about 0.007 gram) and it has the peculiar effect of stimulating the formation of red blood cells in the bone marrow. Some inhabitants of Central Europe actually take small doses of As_4O_6 to improve their complexions, and to increase their work capacity in mountainous regions where the air is thin and more hemoglobin is needed.

Oxidizing arsenic(III) oxide with hot nitric acid or any other strong oxidizing agent produces arsenic(V) oxide, which has the formula As_4O_{10} (like the common oxide of phosphorus, P_4O_{10}). This oxide is more soluble in water than As_4O_6, and is a stronger acid ($K_1 = 5 \times 10^{-3}$). Both distinctions are to be expected, for elements in higher oxidation states form compounds which are more covalent and less basic than those in lower oxidation states. The alkali arsenates again are soluble, but lead arsenate (which is a common insecticide) is highly insoluble. Arsenic(V) oxide does not dissolve readily in hydrochloric acid, but $AsCl_5$ in complexed form can be made by treatment of the element with excess chlorine at moderate temperatures. The pentahalides are more volatile than the trihalides, again reflecting their more covalent character.

Arsine, AsH_3, is a very toxic gas with an unpleasant smell. It was discovered by Scheele in 1755, when he found that arsenic acid, H_3AsO_4, acted on zinc but produced a hydride and zinc arsen*ite*, not zinc arsenate:

$$12\,Zn + 9\,H_3AsO_4 \rightarrow AsH_3 + 4\,Zn_3(AsO_3)_2 + 12\,H_2O$$

The action of zinc on an acid solution containing some soluble compound of arsenic remains the best way to make arsine today, and the hydride can easily be separated from the accompanying large volume of hydrogen by cooling the gases in liquid nitrogen and condensing out the arsine (bp -62.4°C). The pure substance does not decompose in light, but if water vapor is present the hydride soon

76

dissociates into hydrogen and black arsenic. As would be expected from a hydride of a metalloid, arsine is a poor electron donor and does not coordinate to protons in water the way nitrogen does in forming the NH_4^+ ion, or phosphorus does in forming the PH_4^+ ion. Organic derivatives such as dimethylarsine, $(CH_3)_2AsH$, are readily formed and are equally poisonous; the gas given off by the action of mold on old wallpaper colored with arsenate pigments is not really arsine, as is claimed in some detective stories, but trimethylarsine (which is equally injurious to the occupants of the room).

ANTIMONY

There is a distinct change between arsenic and antimony in the fifth group, a change comparable to that between germanium and tin in the neighboring fourth group. Antimony is considerably more metallic in its physical and chemical properties than arsenic. For example, it does not form any organometallic hydrides like the methyl arsines just mentioned. It was thought for a long time to exist only in a silvery *metallic* form (mp 630°C, bp 1440°C, density 6.69, with an electrical conductivity only 4% that of silver), but now is recognized also in an unstable yellow form (density = 5.3), stable only below −90°C. When the metallic form is deposited by electrolysis from a solution of antimony chloride in hydrochloric acid, the deposit contains considerable chloride and is called "explosive" antimony; if it is scratched or struck it changes from its metastable expanded form to ordinary gray antimony, releasing clouds of chloride and considerable heat. Powdered antimony reacts rapidly with chlorine, with a fine display of sparks, but it is not easily oxidized, and it decomposes steam only at red heat. It is converted by boiling nitric acid to the oxyacid H_3SbO_4, which forms a series of antimonate salts.

The black or dark gray sulfide of antimony, Sb_2S_3, is a prominent and widespread mineral. In the powdered form it was used by ancient people as a body paint, and then by the Egyptians to color their eyebrows (Partington also quotes the Vulgate translation of the Bible to the effect that Jezebel painted her eyelids with it). The black pigment came from Arabia, where it was called *mestem*, then *stimmi*, and then *stibi*, whence the name "stibnite" and the symbol Sb have come. The sulfide is easily reduced, and indeed even native metallic antimony is fairly common, which explains why the metal was known and used in ancient times. It probably was confused with lead, and

77

even used in combination with lead, until it was differentiated by the alchemists of the fifteenth and sixteenth centuries.

Much more antimony is produced than arsenic, because antimony is a valuable constituent of alloys. In the proportion of 15% it hardens and strengthens the lead used in storage batteries, and it also reduces the melting points of lead and tin. Some common low-melting alloys which depend upon antimony are *pewter* (7.1% Sb, 89.3% Sn, 1.8% Cu, 1.8% Bi), *type metal* (60% Pb, 30% Sb, 10% Sn), *linotype alloy* (83.5% Pb, 13.5% Sb, 3% Sn), and *bearing metal* (8% Sb, 12% Sn, 80% Pb).

Antimony has three oxides: the tan Sb_2O_3, which is soluble in concentrated sulfuric acid and also in sodium carbonate solution; the white Sb_2O_4, which is soluble in strong alkalies but not in acids, and the yellow Sb_2O_5, which is decidedly acidic. Sodium antimonate is used to flameproof cloth, and various other antimonates are used to impart a yellow color to glass, pottery, and ceramic enamels.

Antimony forms a volatile, smelly, and poisonous hydride called stibine, SbH_3, which forms under the same conditions used to produce arsine in the Marsh test. In order to differentiate between deposits of arsenic and antimony in that test, four tests are used:

(1) Antimony deposits on the glass tube as a dark mirror *before* the region of the flame, not after it, as arsenic does (thereby reflecting the lower thermal stability of stibine vs. arsine).

(2) When the deposit is moistened with a drop of ammonium sulfide solution and warmed, arsenic leaves a yellow residue of As_2S_3, but antimony leaves orange Sb_2S_3.

(3) If a drop of sodium or calcium hypochlorite solution is applied to the deposit, arsenic dissolves by the reaction

$$10\,NaClO + 6\,H_2O + As_4 \rightarrow 10\,NaCl + 4\,H_3AsO_4$$

but antimony does not react.

(4) Arsenic is insoluble in a concentrated solution of tartaric acid, but antimony dissolves to form a basic tartrate, $(SbO)_2C_4H_4O_6$.

These reactions give a good indication of the chemical behavior of antimony vs. that of arsenic, as well as eliminating the ambiguities of the Marsh test. In general, arsenic resembles nitrogen and phosphorus a great deal in chemical behavior, but antimony resembles bismuth, a true metal.

78

THE HEALING ARTS

We come now to chemotherapy, the treatment of disease by means of specific chemical agents synthesized for the purpose. In the progress of the healing arts from pure magic and voodooism to the present intricate science of medicine, many natural remedies have become recognized as effective against particular pathological conditions. Thus we have quinine to combat malaria, digitalis to relieve heart congestion, opiates to reduce pain, and so on and on through the thousands of certified drugs listed in the U. S. Pharmacopoeia. The remedies mentioned there are by no means all plant products, nor all organic; such thoroughly inorganic substances as zinc oxide, calomel, bismuth subnitrate, and magnesium hydroxide also have their places in the traditional arsenal of physicians' weapons. These thousands of medicines are not enough, however; there are many diseases still to be conquered, and more specific agents are needed—many more than are in the natural world around us, it would seem.

The toxic effects of some elements being what they are, it was inevitable that the beneficial or healing effects of mercury, silver, arsenic, and antimony should have been recognized thousands of years ago. In modern times we explain that these elements (or their compounds) are toxic to the microorganisms that cause some diseases, and so are beneficial in their proper places. In previous ages, however, there was no germ theory of disease, but only the accumulated experience of what was beneficial and what was not. Some of this experience was written down in the medical literature of the time. Thus the great medieval physician Theophrastus Bombastus von Hohenheim (1490–1541), who called himself Paracelsus, wrote in his "Practica" (1529) of the proper use of arsenic, antimony, mercury, and lead in the treatment of disease. Paracelsus believed thoroughly in making whatever Nature did not supply for his purpose, but he had little opportunity to prove the effectiveness of his preparations (other than the dubious method of trying them on isolated human patients) because he did not believe in animal experimentation and had no research facilities.

The idea of synthesizing specific reagents for various pathogenic organisms persisted in haphazard fashion for nearly four centuries more before it was given both a working theory and a clear reduction to practice by Paul Ehrlich in 1910. Ehrlich was both a bacteriologist and an expert organic chemist, one who did a great deal of research on the molecular design and the synthesis of new aniline dyes. He prepared new dyes to stain microorganisms so that they would be more clearly visible under the microscope, and he recognized very early that an effective dye needed a chemically reactive group which would fix it to the side chains of the particular protoplasm to be colored. He discovered a dye called *trypan red* which not only dyed trypanosomes red but also interfered with their propagation, even in the living host. For this important discovery he received the Nobel Prize in medicine in 1908. It was *after* this that he formulated his three great principles of chemotherapy, which gave clear meaning to the word and clear directions for conducting research. These principles are:

1) A chemotherapeutic agent must be highly specific, and in an ideal case will be so specific as to be effective against only one kind of microorganism. This is necessary because the agent must be taken up by the microorganism in sufficient quantity for lethal action, but at the same time must not harm the host.

2) A chemotherapeutic agent needs a "chemoreceptor" group as part of its molecular architecture, a group which attaches itself specifically to certain unique or characteristic parts of the organism's protoplasm. This is the "specificity" idea derived from the specific attachment of certain dyes to particular fibers, or of trypan red to the proteins of trypanosomes.

3) A chemotherapeutic agent must be delivered to the site of infection in effective concentration, and therefore needs attention directed to its solubility in appropriate body fluids at the time it is designed. Some sites of infection will be insulated from the agent by calciferous deposits or fibrous tissue, and these will be harder to treat. A blood infection, on the other hand, should be easier for an agent to attack. Hence some kinds of infection are more amenable to chemotherapeutic treatment than others, and a sensible target should be chosen for what Ehrlich called the "magic bullets" (the molecules of chemotherapeutic agent).

Using the well-known toxicity of arsenic as a sound starting point, Ehrlich sought to clothe the lethal atoms in an appropriate organic garb which would deliver the arsenic to the site of infection and fix it to the spirochetes which cause syphilis. He and his co-workers made and tested 605 compounds before they arrived at the chemotherapeutic agent they wanted, No. 606, which they named Salvarsan.

80

It is a *bis*-phenyl diarsine, specifically 3,3'-diamino-4,4'-dihydroxyar-senobenzene.

This substance, given repeatedly in a prescribed course of treatment, was the first effective agent the world had ever known against the terrible scourge of syphilis. While neither absolutely specific, nor totally without side-effects on the patient, it did its job and did it well. Ehrlich replaced it later with "Neoarsphenamine," a less toxic arsenical with a solublizing group of the structure—$NHCH_2SO_2Na$ in place of one of the amino groups, and this remained the most effective weapon against spirochetes for many years.

The reader may well ask how such compounds are made. There are many routes to Salvarsan, but one possible synthesis starts with the preparation of an aryldichloroarsine from a Grignard reagent

$$RMgCl + AsCl_3 \rightarrow RAsCl_2 + MgCl_2$$

followed by appropriate substitution of the aryl group and then hydrolysis to the corresponding oxide

$$x\,RAsCl_2 + x\,H_2O \rightarrow (RAsO)_x + 2x\,HCl$$

The arylarsenic oxide is written in polymeric form because such substances usually are of high molecular weight and insoluble in benzene, with a high and variable melting point (all signs of a polymeric structure As—O—As—O—, etc.).* The oxide then is reduced with sodium hydrosulfite or hypophosphorous acid or other strong reducing agent to form the diarsine:

$$2\,(RAsO)_x + 2x \text{ units of reducing agent} \rightarrow x\,RAs{=}AsR + 2x\,H_2O$$

An unsymmetrical diarsine of the type used in Neoarsphenamine can be made by reducing the appropriate arylarsenic oxide with the correct arylarsine:

$$x\,RAsH_2 + (R'AsO)_x \rightarrow x\,RAs{=}AsR' + x\,H_2O$$

---

* A lower-melting form of C_6H_5AsO is known (mp 142°C to 145°C), but this may be a hydroxide.

It is not known whether the structures of Arsphenamine and Neo-arsphenamine really involve double bonds between arsenic atoms as shown in the formulas. If the bonds *are* multiple, they probably are not classical double bonds such as exist in ethene, but rather are somewhat metallic in nature. All that is known is that the empirical formula is as shown, and that *bis*-phenyl diarsine is associated. The degree of association varies with the solvent, being 2.1 in naphthalene, 1.5 in benzene, and 1.1 in carbon disulfide.* If the substance is a dimer, it could be written with a square of four arsenic atoms, but in view of the changing degree of association this seems artificial.

After Ehrlich proved his point and launched the science of chemo-therapy, an exhaustive search was made during the period 1910 to 1935 for other curative agents among the thousands of possible organic derivatives of arsenic, antimony, and mercury. Some of the results of this search show up today in drugs and bactericides such as Mer-curochrome (2,7-dibromo-4-hydroxymercurifluorescein) and Merthio-late (sodium ethylmercury thiosalicylate). Organometallic diuretics also appeared, and organometallic agents to protect seeds from fungus and disease before germination. Emphasis then switched to the sulfanilamide drugs, which were synthesized in the laboratory accord-ing to the true chemotherapeutic tradition and which interfered specifically with the metabolism of certain classes of bacteria. Then, since man does not have a monopoly on clever or complicated organic syntheses, the emphasis switched to the more subtle antibiotics syn-thesized by certain mold organisms. The first of these was the sub-stance which Fleming discovered and named *penicillin*. This substance comes remarkably close to Ehrlich's ideal, being 200 times as effective as sulfanilamide against certain types of bacteria, and yet with a very low inherent toxicity for mammals. It was difficult to produce in quantity, but its success was so great that an intensive search was made for other antibiotics which could be made by microbial syn-thesis. There now are many effective ones, such as aureomycin, terramycin, bacitracin, neomycin, and the oxytetracyclines. A two-page table in the *McGraw-Hill Encyclopedia of Science and Technology*, volume 1, page 466, lists 38 such antibiotics, together with the organisms they attack and the diseases they combat. A further table, on page 468 of the same article, shows the dramatic

---

* E. G. Rochow, D. T. Hurd, and R. N. Lewis, *The Chemistry of Organometallic Compounds*, Chap. 8, p. 211, Wiley, New York, 1957.

decrease in death rates due to pneumonia, tuberculosis, influenza, syphilis, appendicitis, and rheumatic fever which attended the introduction of these chemotherapeutic agents.

It is not the purpose of this short discussion to review all the present fields of chemotherapy, or even to list all its past triumphs, but merely to point out what a potent tool of the intellect was fashioned by Paul Ehrlich half a century ago, and what part arsenic played in all this. The battle against disease goes on, and organic derivatives of the metalloids will probably figure in it again and again. Whether that comes about or not, this introduction should lead the ambitious premedical student to study both the history and the present progress of chemotherapy.

CHAPTER 7

A Little about Selenium and Tellurium

Selenium and tellurium are two rare elements, one-fiftieth and one three-thousandth as abundant as arsenic, respectively. Selenium exists both in a red nonmetallic allotrope and as a gray metalloid, the conductivity of which increases with the intensity of light falling on it. Tellurium exists in a reddish-brown amorphous form and as a metalloid. Both elements are of interest here because they form *weak* bonds to most other elements, in sharp contrast to the behavior of boron, silicon, and germanium.

Selenium occasionally is found in the natural elementary state, as is sulfur, but the most plentiful supply is in the form of selenides of copper, silver, mercury, and lead. Of these, the most common is berzelianite, Cu_2Se, named after the famous chemist J. J. Berzelius, who discovered selenium in 1817. The selenides which occur in copper and lead ores are driven off as selenium or its oxides during roasting and smelting operations. Both the element and its oxides may be absorbed by plants, which thereby become poisonous to animals. To obtain elementary selenium for use, selenide minerals are heated with sulfuric acid and the filtered solution is concentrated and cooled until selenious acid (H_2SeO_3) crystallizes. When the crystals are dissolved in water and sulfur dioxide is bubbled into the solution, a precipitate of brick-red selenium forms.

Red selenium has two modifications, the more common of which melts at 144°C and has a density of 4.42. This is soluble in carbon disulfide in the form of Se_8 molecules, which have a puckered ring structure exactly like the S_8 molecules of crystalline sulfur. If the dry red selenium is warmed to 80°C it slowly changes over to the gray metalloidal form, which has a density of 4.82, melts at 220°C, and boils at 685°C.

It is the gray form which is used in selenium photocells and selenium rectifiers, of course. This form has a conductivity which is nearly proportional to the square root of the intensity of light falling upon it, and therefore, when a layer of gray selenium is deposited on a metal plate and covered by a very thin transparent film of evaporated aluminum, the combination becomes a photoconductive device. It should be emphasized that such a cell regulates current according to lighting conditions purely because of its resistive function; it is not a photovoltaic cell. For a given intensity, red light is more effective than other colors. The selenium photocell was very popular for a time, and still has its uses, but it competes rather poorly with the cesium vacuum photovoltaic cell and the silicon solar battery.

When selenium dioxide or sodium selenate is dissolved in silicate glass and then slowly reduced by a flame, it imparts a ruby-red color to the glass. This is the source of the deep red glass used in signal-light lenses, and it comes from a slow reduction and heat treatment of the glass to obtain just the right dispersion of colloidal red selenium. At much lower concentration a faint yellow or reddish color is obtained. If properly controlled, just enough selenium color can be imparted to bottle glass to counteract the green color due to dissolved iron in the glass, for the two colors are complementary. This "decolorizing" of glass is considered important for milk bottles and food jars, where green glass would give the wrong impression. Selenium has taken over the job from manganese dioxide, which formerly was relied upon to give a pink Mn(II) color when reduced. It should be emphasized that the selenium remains locked in the glass, and does not contaminate the contents.

Some selenium also is used for vulcanizing special rubber compositions, and occasionally in lead and iron alloys. Other than the use in glass, there are no consumer uses, because selenium and its compounds are very poisonous. Moreover, the compounds with hydrogen, oxygen, and the halogens all decompose rather readily, so that they are not durable enough for application. To add a final blow, the hydride H_2Se and all the volatile organoselenium compounds have *very* unpleasant odors, so that they do not lend themselves to applications near people.

Tellurium acts a great deal like selenium, except that its compounds are still less stable and its general behavior is more nearly like that of a metal. Its elementary forms are (1) a poorly-understood and unstable red or brown form, of density 6.02, precipitated by reduction of telluric acid in water solution, and (2) the well-known silver-white form which is isomorphous with gray selenium. The conductivity of this metallic form changes very little when it is illuminated. It melts at 450°C, boils at 1390°C, and has a density of 6.25. It is insoluble in carbon disulfide and in all other unreactive solvents.

Tellurium is sometimes added to steel to make it draw more easily in stamping operations, and it is added to lead to make it stronger and more durable. It imparts a brownish color to glass, but is not used much in this way. Tellurium-vulcanized rubber is very tough, and so outdoor power cables sometimes are sheathed in such rubber. The compounds of tellurium are very toxic, and its hydride and organic derivatives are said to smell even worse than those of selenium.

A final aspect of selenium and tellurium, and one which is very informative about the nature of these elements, is their organometallic chemistry. It is an axiom of chemistry that bonds which are easy to break are easy to form, so that the preparation of organoselenium and organotellurium compounds is exceptionally easy. As one example, dimethylselenium can be made in 88% yield from elemental selenium and methyl iodide *in water*, using an alkaline solution of rongalite (a formaldehyde compound of sodium sulfoxylate, $HCHO \cdot NaHSO_2$) as reducing agent to remove the iodine:

$$Se + 2\,CH_3I + HCHO \cdot NaHSO_2 + NaOH \rightarrow$$
$$(CH_3)_2Se + 2\,NaI + SO_2 + H_2O + HCHO$$

The same reaction goes still more easily with tellurium, requiring only sodium sulfite as reducing agent in the alkaline solution:

$$Te + 2\,(C_2H_5)_2I + Na_2SO_3 + Na_2CO_3 \rightarrow$$
$$(C_2H_5)_2Te + 2\,NaI + CO_2 + Na_2SO_4$$

The reader will find *very* few organometallic compounds that can be prepared in aqueous solution; those of selenium, tellurium, and mercury are about the only ones. Just to show that the first two are even less active than mercury, as defined by Gilman's Rules (see

Chapter 3), consider the reaction by which selenium alkyls are made from mercury alkyls:

$$2 SeX_4 + 3 R_2Hg \rightarrow 2 R_2Se + 3 HgX_2 + 2 RX$$

Elementary selenium is acted upon even by the Grignard Reagent, not as an active metal replacing magnesium in the reagent, but rather as a negative element forming a metal salt of the magnesium:

$$Se + C_2H_5MgBr \text{ (in ether) } \rightarrow C_2H_5SeMgBr$$

Hydrolysis then gives the organoselenium hydride:

$$C_2H_5SeMgBr + HCl \rightarrow C_2H_5SeH + MgBrCl$$

This is acidic, as are the hydrides of all rather negative elements, and can be neutralized by a base:

$$C_2H_5SeH + NaOH \rightarrow C_2H_5SeNa + H_2O$$

The resulting sodium salt will undergo an exchange reaction (metathesis) with an alkyl halide, here methyl iodide, to give a selenium alkyl:

$$C_2H_5SeNa + CH_3I \rightarrow C_2H_5SeCH_3 + NaI$$

From such simple inorganic reagents, plus a source of alkyl or aryl groups, the organometalloidal derivatives of selenium and tellurium can be made at room temperature.

The last equation indicates that metal selenides and tellurides also should react with alkyl halides to make organometalloidal derivatives, and this conclusion is supported by two well-known preparations. The first involves the use of sodium selenide or telluride, which reacts with organic sulfonates (derivatives of sulfuric acid, in which one hydrogen atom of H_2SO_4 is replaced by an alkyl or aryl group):

$$Na_2Se + 2 C_2H_5OSO_3Na \rightarrow (C_2H_5)_2Se + 2 Na_2SO_4$$
$$Na_2Te + 2 C_4H_9OSO_3Na \rightarrow (C_4H_9)_2Te + 2 Na_2SO_4$$

The second preparation makes use of aluminum telluride, which reacts with ordinary alcohols to make organotellurium compounds:

$$Al_2Te_3 + 6 C_2H_5OH \rightarrow 3 (C_2H_5)_2Te + 2 Al(OH)_3$$

This reaction is reminiscent of the hydrolysis of aluminum carbide to give methane and other hydrocarbons.

Table 7.1

Some Organic Derivatives of Selenium and Tellurium

Compound	Mp, °C	Bp, °C	Density
$(CH_3)_2Se$	—	55	1.401
$(CH_3)_2Te$	—	82	—
$(C_2H_5)_2Se$	—	108	1.230
$(C_2H_5)_2Te$	—	137	1.599
$(C_6H_5)_2Se$	2.5	301	1.356
$(C_6H_5)_2Te$	4.2	174 at 10 mm	1.566
$(CH_3)_2Se_2$	—	152	—
$(C_6H_5)_2Se_2$	63.5	203 at 11 mm	—
$(C_6H_5)_2Te_2$	53.4	—	—
C_2H_5SeH	53.2	—	1.3594

A small selection of organoselenium and organotellurium compounds is listed in Table 7.1.

With all this ease of preparation and purification, it would give a great deal of satisfaction to be able to apply organoselenium and organotellurium compounds to many practical purposes. Unfortunately, they have no uses whatever. Organotellurium compounds do a fair job of raising the octane number of gasoline, but they were superseded by tetraethyllead for this job. The odor and toxicity of selenium and tellurium compounds militate against any widespread use, and so this chapter will have to conclude on a note of chemical knowledge just for its own sake.

CHAPTER **8**

Some Projections into the Future

The foregoing discussion of the metalloids, both individually and collectively, has brought together a great deal of chemical information which would otherwise have remained diverse and disconnected. Quite of necessity, the subject has drawn upon segments of inorganic, organic, physical, and practical chemistry. Various uses of the metalloid elements and their compounds were brought into the discussion to illustrate points of theory or deduction, and so it is hoped that the reader already understands the industrial and consumer uses of the various substances and materials mentioned. However, it is appropriate at this time to look into the future and to inquire what effects the metalloids and their derivatives will have on the scientific and the popular progress of our people during the next few decades.

One of the matters which comes to the fore at once is the question of boron-containing fuels for jet aircraft or for rockets. This question arose in 1945, pursued a pattern of research, development, and pilot-plant trials up to 1960 or so, and then was dropped quite suddenly. "Exotic fuels," as they were called in the popular press, had just about come to the public attention (at least enough to influence the stock market) when they disappeared from the scene. What were the reasons? Is there any justification for boron-based fuels, on any practical scale? What would happen if they were to come into widespread use?

There is no doubt whatever about the thermochemical advantage of the boron hydrides over the carbon hydrides, as fuels. Burning one gram of boron* generates 13 kilocalories, whereas burning one

---

* to B_2O_3 glass at 18°C.

89

gram of carbon* generates 7.9 kilocalories. It follows that burning one gram of B_2H_6 will give more than twice as much heat as burning one gram of C_2H_6, especially since B_2H_6 comes apart more readily (that is, less must be subtracted from the heats of combustion of boron and hydrogen for the dissociation of the B_2H_6 molecules). The same could be said for B_5H_8 vs. C_4H_{10}, or any other comparison. The main point is that the more boron there is in a fuel, the greater will be the thermochemical advantage in terms of calories obtained per unit weight of fuel consumed.

Since the lower hydrides of boron are gases, they would be inconvenient fuels for airplanes. Two stable boranes, B_5H_9 and B_6H_{10}, are liquid at room temperature, but decaborane, $B_{10}H_{14}$, is a crystalline solid melting at about 100°C. It follows that if boranes are to be used as fuels for transportation, pentaborane and hexaborane would have to be the candidates. But the available methods of synthesis all make diborane, B_2H_6, and hence this would have to be converted to the two desirable boranes. Realizing this, an intensive study of conversion processes was begun, and while the results are not completely available because of military importance of the project, it may be assumed that conversions of rather unstable but expensive boranes would lead to considerable losses and much more expense, putting an obstacle in the way of the development. Any widespread use of the boranes also would have to take into consideration their toxicity, which would be a powerfully antagonistic factor. It also must be pointed out that the most volatile boranes ignite spontaneously upon exposure to air, which might be an advantage in some types of engine but presents a definite hazard in storage and transport. Although the liquid boranes do not inflame as readily as diborane, because of lower vapor pressure, they have a similar tendency to do so. These factors combine to work against the use of the boranes themselves.

It is possible that some of the objections to boranes might be overcome (or reduced) by incorporating boron into hydrocarbon structures, or by using boron alkyls in place of the hydrides. Trimethylboron, for example, is much more stable than the boranes and does not have the toxicity of the boranes, although it does ignite spontaneously in air. Two chief difficulties arise in connection with this proposal to use boron alkyls. The first involves the expense of syn-

---

* to CO_2 gas at 18°C.

thesis; there is no direct synthesis from boron, so that it is necessary to go through boron trichloride, using Grignard reagents and ether to attach the alkyl groups. Second, the boron alkyls are very volatile, and it would be necessary to use something like tripropylborane, $(C_3H_7)_3B$ (mp $-65.5°C$, bp $164.5°C$), in a jet engine. But tripropylborane is only 7.8% boron by weight, so the thermochemical advantage of boron has almost disappeared. For these reasons the proposal to use boron alkyls as fuels has come to nothing.

There remains the possibility of synthesizing and using organic modifications of the higher boranes, modifications which (hopefully) might make them liquid and improve them in other ways. The boranes based on completed (or nearly completed) icosahedral or dodecahedral structures would seem to be the best candidates, in view of their inherent stabilities and very high boron contents. The carboranes mentioned in Chapter 4 represent a start in this direction, but the substances are rare and expensive at the time of writing, and no one would consider using them as fuels. Not yet. They may very well become commercially important, but in more highly specialized ways, and not likely as fuels.

What would happen if boron-containing fuels were to be used on a large scale? It does not take much chemical perspicacity to point out two matters of some importance:

1) Boron is a rare element, and although we are blessed with some concentrated sources of it in this country (in the form of borax in dried-up western lakes), we would soon run out of it if we attempted to use it on a scale comparable to that for gasoline or even jet fuel. The earth's crust is only 0.0003% boron, and it is not concentrated in convenient reduced form as is coal or petroleum, but rather in oxidized form that requires much expensive reduction. Furthermore, if we were to burn the boron in aircraft it would be scattered quite literally to the four winds, and we could not recover it.

2) We must take into account that the combustion product of the boron used in the proposed fuels would be B_2O_3 or its hydrate, boric acid. We know from much sad experience in hospitals where boric acid has been mistaken (so easily!) for dextrose and maltose that boric acid is a lethal poison to infants, and indeed to everyone. The prospect of scattering tons of boric acid above our major cities each day, as hundreds of jet aircraft take off, is very un-

91

pleasant to contemplate. Yet there is nothing else that can be done with the combustion product. We would have to breathe it. The rest would drift around, wash down with the rains, and get into water supplies and crops in undesirable amounts. Quite properly, there would be a great fuss.

With these two points in mind, the prospect does not look favorable for boron-base fuels in commercial quantities. There is still a possibility that their use in a very limited way for purely military purposes might be justified, but not for commercial transport.

There remains a "dividend" from research on boranes which may well achieve great importance in the next ten or twenty years: the carboranes. As pointed out in Chapter 4, the carboranes are cage-structure higher boranes with one, two, or more boron atoms substituted by carbon atoms. Since carbon has one electron more than boron, such structures usually "prefer" the state of a negative ion, such as $B_{10}C_2H_{10}{}^{2-}$ (the neutral compound $B_{10}C_2H_{12}$ is a strong acid). Since the completed icosahedron behaves as a unit and persists in reactions, a considerable case can be built up for it (as Earl Muetterties has done) as a future counterpart of the benzene ring. This is to say that the basic carborane structure undoubtedly will have many derivatives and variations, all with a chemical behavior quite different from anything that has been known before. An entirely new branch of chemistry will develop, with its own triumphs and novelties. Already there have been some patents issued, and probably we can look forward to some entirely new dyes, drugs, fibers, plastics, or elastomers designed around the carborane framework. All of this may indeed turn out to be more important than the fuel project that did not materialize.

Concerning silicon, little more need be said beyond that which already has appeared in the discussions concerning silicon rectifiers, transistors, and solar cells, plus silicone resins, oils, elastomers, and protective films, plus glass and ceramics. A considerable part of this book has dealt with silicon, simply because there is so much of it, so much chemical knowledge about it, and so much accumulated experience in making useful things from it. Looking into the future, we can expect that many more new things and new materials will be made from it. Being so abundant, so nontoxic, and so dependable in forming strong chemical bonds in so many diverse ways, it is inevitable that silicon will be exploited more and more. A few particular points might be made:

1) Continued rapid expansion of the solid-state electronics field is to be expected. Now that transistors have displaced vacuum tubes from so many of their applications, electronic circuits have been freed from the necessity of hot cathodes and from cathode heating power, and also from the requirement of high-voltage supplies. As a result, electronic devices can be made smaller, lighter, and more durable than before, and so they are now capable of doing more jobs than they were able to do before. The effects of liberation from large power requirements are just beginning to be felt, so that interesting developments are to be expected in the near future.

2) Solar cells and batteries, although they really represent a part of the solid-state electronics aspect of silicon, are beginning to achieve a separate importance. Already they have become the sole source of power for communications satellites and many other space-exploration vehicles (in short, for all nonearthbound devices that have a long-term power requirement). The brilliant sunshine of interplanetary space makes such cells a logical source of electricity. As space exploration proceeds and space travel develops, the demand for more and better solar batteries will increase very rapidly. Present devices use something under a hundred square feet of silicon cells exposed to the sun; future space stations probably will expose acres of silicon surface in the same way. What is needed most at present is an *inexpensive* way of making single-crystal films or wafers of very pure silicon, instead of growing single crystals and then sawing them up. Present moves in this direction center around epitaxial growth of single-crystal regions by depositing silicon from the thermal decomposition of SiH_4. This represents one major change in technique; others would be welcome. (Fig. 8.0).

3) The further development of organosilicon chemistry will lead to cheaper silicone polymers, and hence to new uses and to more widespread use of the present materials. Figure 8.1 shows how things have been going during the recent past; extension of the same trends into the near future seems justified, in the absence of any abrupt disturbance. Silicones will become cheaper and will be used in much larger quantities, in many new ways (Fig. 8.2).

4) Other chemical uses of silicon *as a raw material* are to be expected, now that silicones have shown the way. Silicon is so versatile a substance, in a chemical way, that many new things could be done

93

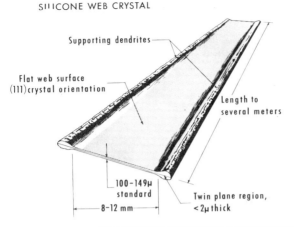

SILICONE WEB CRYSTAL

Supporting dendrites

Flat web surface
(111) crystal orientation

Length to
several meters

100-149μ
standard

8-12 mm

Twin plane region,
< 2μ thick

Figure 8.0 Silicon crystal of any desired length up to several meters is grown as a thin web between two thick-section supporting members (dendrites). The designation "111 face" refers to the Miller indices of classical crystallography; a 100 face of a cubic crystal like this one intercepts one axis but is parallel to the other two axes, while a 111 face intercepts all three crystallographic axes equidistant from their origin.

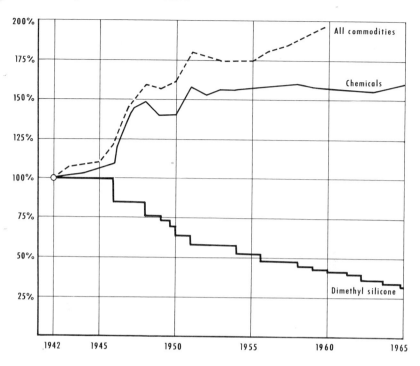

Figure 8.1 Price reductions of dimethyl silicone *vs.* price advances for chemicals and other commodities. (Data for dimethyl silicone courtesy of Mr. P. K. Blumer of Dow Corning Corp., Midland, Michigan; other data from Bureau of Labor Statistics as reported in *Chemical and Engineering News*.)

with it.* The shackles of traditional thinking, centered principally around carbon chemistry, are the chief handicap here. When students learn more about silicon and its possibilities, there will be more done with silicon.

Plotting the future course of development of germanium is a much more difficult task. Germanium is the traditional peer of semiconductor materials; probably more is known about its electrical properties than about those of any other element. About 100 million transistors are made from it each year. Yet in a practical way it has

---

* See *Unnatural Products: New and Useful Materials from Silicon*, Priestly Lectures for 1960, by E. G. Rochow (Phi Lambda Upsilon and the Pennsylvania State University, University Park, Pa., 1960).

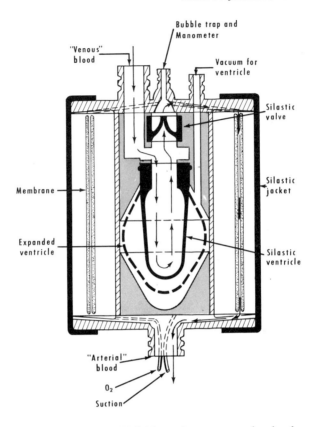

Figure 8.2 A new type of artificial heart-lung, now under development at the National Institutes of Health, Bethesda, Maryland, uses a membrane of *Silastic* silicone rubber, reinforced with Dacron fabric, as the oxygenating surface for blood. The blood flows over one side of the membrane as oxygen bathes the other side. The thin film of silicone rubber allows oxygen molecules to diffuse through to the venous blood, releasing carbon dioxide which permeates the membrane in the other direction. Blood circulation is maintained by a vacuum-operated silicone rubber pump.

yielded some of its jobs to silicon, for reasons developed in Chapter 2. Undoubtedly germanium will continue to be used in common kinds of transistors for many years to come, and it is quite likely that new solid-state electronic devices will make their first appearance in a germanium form. So the tradition of germanium will continue.

On the chemical side, there are no present chemical applications

96

from which to extrapolate. Recent research has shown some possibilities for future exploitation which can be summarized in this way:

1) Organogermanium compounds show a very low-order but definite toxicity toward microorganisms, coupled with a large tolerance by mammals. This is a promising beginning for developing a chemotherapy of germanium, and wide-open possibilities beckon.

2) Germanium shows some interesting possibilities as a constituent of alloys. It has a greater solubility in metals than silicon has, and so can be used in greater quantity to contribute its hardness and its acid resistance. It makes copper hard and tough, and gives it a gold appearance. It contributes hardness and permanence to dental alloys, plus one other important property: gold-germanium alloys expand on freezing, and so produce a sharp impression. Alloys of germanium with silver which have almost zero temperature coefficient of resistance have been developed for use in evaporated-film resistors.

3) Infrared lenses and filters made of elementary germanium are made in limited number, and germanium glasses occasionally have their specialty uses. If greater demands are made on optical equipment in the future, germanium is likely to figure in the new devices.

In the fifth group, if there are to be any expanded uses of arsenic, they are most likely to come in the area of materials which do not expose the arsenic to the consumer. Any further use in glass or in alloys would meet this requirement. It is possible, of course, that the vast amount of accumulated information on organic arsenicals will someday prove useful again in some phase of chemotherapy, or in external control of microorganisms.

The future of antimony seems to lie in new alloys, where its properties of low melting point, hardness, and expansion on freezing will probably always be in demand. There probably also will be more use of antimonate flame-proofing agents, which will become more important as the continuing campaign to reduce the danger of fire proceeds. The further use of antimony in fluorescent lamp phosphors and in semiconductor devices also is a possibility.

In the sixth group, the cards seem stacked against selenium and tellurium. Yet this is just the kind of situation that reveals the unreliability of forecasts and forecasters; by its very nature, a true discovery cannot be forecast. Some entirely new piece of information, or a need suddenly defined clearly, may result in an application which was not dreamed of—for the simple reason that there was no basis for a dream. When someone says, "There can be no further progress in such-and-such," that is the time to look for a breakthrough. We have only 89 elements in quantities we can see. In the future we are sure to need every one of them for its special properties.

CHAPTER **9**

Suggestions for Further Reading

A book of this sort can do little more than arouse the interest of the student. If he responds, and becomes interested in the metalloids, the next step is to go on to higher-level sources of information, where much more complete accounts are available. The purpose of this chapter is to make the transition easy by suggesting a graded sequence of references. The list is not exhaustive, nor does it represent the only pathway to an expert understanding of the subject. It merely lists some literature sources which will not disappoint the student, and which will take him to the edge of the research frontier if he likes.

Usually there is one particular aspect of the electrical or chemical behavior of the metalloids which beckons to the student. If so, it is best for him to pursue that specific interest further at first, learning all he can by reading references and by direct observation. A good first source of information on specific topics is the 15-volume *McGraw-Hill Encyclopedia of Science and Technology*, McGraw-Hill Book Co., New York, 1960, which is available in most general and chemistry libraries. This encyclopedia has an excellent index, and every year a new Yearbook is issued which serves to keep the information up to date. There also are extensive reading lists given at the end of each article. Since it covers *all* the sciences and their technology, this encyclopedia is particularly useful in connection with an interdisciplinary subject like the metalloids.

There will come a time, perhaps quite soon, when the student finds that he cannot pursue his favorite interest further without understanding the fundamentals of chemistry and physics. This is the time to start serious study with a more advanced book. Quite likely the first requirement will be some book on inorganic chemistry which packs a great deal of organized, comparative information on the metalloid elements and their compounds, but which can be read after a year or so of college chemistry. Such a book is Therald Moeller's *Inorganic Chemistry: An Advanced Textbook*, 966 pp., John Wiley & Sons, New York, 1952. This may soon be issued in a revised two-volume edition by the same publisher.

The mineral chemistry of the metalloids and the details of their extraction are matters which have been squeezed out of modern textbooks but are readily found in the older books such as J. R. Partington's *A Text-Book of Inorganic Chemistry*, 6th ed., 996 pp., McMillan and Co., London, 1950. Alternatively, a book on geochemistry and prospecting such as *Principles of Geochemistry* by B. Mason (2nd ed., 1958), or *Geochemistry* by K. Rankama and T. G. Sahama (1950) will be of value. *Dana's Manual of Mineralogy* (16th ed., by C. S. Hurlbut, Jr., 1952) is a classical and permanently valuable source.

As his reading about the metalloidal elements progresses, the student often will wish that there were one comprehensive summary of absolutely *everything* that is known about one particular element. There is. It is called *Gmelins Handbuch der Anorganischen Chemie*, and is now in its 8th edition, put out by the internationally supported Gmelin Institut in Frankfurt and published by Verlag Chemie GMBH in Weinheim, Germany. It consists of a separate volume (or volumes) on each element, conscientiously compiled by a staff of experts and containing a critical summary of all the physical constants and all the chemical behavior of that element and its compounds up to the date of publication.*

Since many students of chemistry, even graduate students, do not seem to be aware of this monumental and thoroughly reliable work, the reader is urged to make his acquaintance with Gmelin as early as possible. True, it consists of nearly a hundred volumes, but it is organized and systematic. In order to avoid duplication in the treatment of compounds (which necessarily pertain to two or more elements), each element is assigned a System Number, the most common and more negative elements coming first. For example, the

---

* More specifically, up to the date of completion of the manuscript. Some additional information (but not a complete survey) is added in proof.

System Number for boron is 13, that for silicon is 15, that for germanium is 45, and so on. Instead of an index, each volume contains an elaborately detailed table of contents, representing about 7% of the length of the book. The more recent volumes of Gmelin have this table of contents printed in English as well as in German, so that the student with even a very weak knowledge of German can find the constants and the references he is after. Gmelin is a great timesaver and a valuable institution, so every student should be aware of what it can do for him.

If it is theoretical information (rather than factual) that the student seeks, he is not so fortunate as to find everything in one place. Let us suppose that he is interested in the theories of chemical bonding, especially as they apply to the special case of the boron hydrides. He could begin by reading H. H. Sisler's *Electronic Structure, Properties, and the Periodic Law*, 120 pp., Reinhold Publ. Corp., New York, 1963, especially Chapter 2 on "Chemical Bonding as a Function of Attraction for Electrons." After that, and especially after a course in physical chemistry, he could read about the molecular orbital theory (and its rival theories) in *Advanced Inorganic Chemistry*, by F. A. Cotton and G. Wilkinson, Interscience-Wiley, New York, 1962. He might also consult *Theoretical Inorganic Chemistry*, by M. L. Day and J. Selbin, Reinhold Publ. Corp., New York, 1962; and, after more background, C. J. Ballhausen's *Introduction to Ligand Field Theory*, McGraw-Hill Book Co., New York, 1962. The special theoretical aspects of three-center bonds as they apply in boron compounds are treated in detail in the book entitled *Boron Hydrides*, by W. N. Lipscomb, W. A. Benjamin, Inc., New York, 1963.

The structural aspects of compounds of the metalloids are especially important, and can best be studied (after a course in physical chemistry) in the outstanding classical textbook for this field, A. F. Wells' *Structural Inorganic Chemistry*, 3rd ed., 1055 pp., Oxford-Clarendon Press, 1962. The structures of the boranes and related compounds are described in detail in the Lipscomb book noted above. A unique summary of atomic spacings and bond angles for *all* kinds of chemical compounds appears in *Tables of Interatomic Distances and Configuration in Molecules and Ions*, compiled by L. E. Sutton and others (Special Publication No. 11, The Chemical Society, London, 1958).

Further reading on the hydrides of the metalloids can be found in the volume by D. T. Hurd entitled *An Introduction to the Chemistry of the Hydrides*, 231 pp., John Wiley & Sons, New York, 1952; and in *Hydrides of the Group IV Elements*, by F. G. A. Stone, Prentice-Hall, New York, 1961.

The organic derivatives of the metalloids warranted special attention in Chapter 3 and figured prominently in Chapters 5, 6, 7, and 8. No matter whether the student is interested in the historical, factual, medical, theoretical, or practical aspects of the metalloids, he should study organometallic chemistry. The subject is not treated in introductory books, nor in inorganic texts, so he must turn to special references. At a modest level, he could start with *Organometallic Chemistry*, by E. G. Rochow, 112 pp., Reinhold Publ. Corp., New York, 1964; and then advance to *Organo-Metallic Compounds*, by G. E. Coates, 366 pp., 2nd ed., Methuen & Co., London, 1960. Another comprehensive reference is *The Chemistry of Organometallic Compounds*, by E. G. Rochow, D. T. Hurd, and R. N. Lewis, 344 pp., John Wiley & Sons, New York, 1957.

Because of its practical importance, organosilicon chemistry has its own extensive literature, and so deserves some special mention. The reader might start with *An Introduction to the Chemistry of the Silicones*, by E. G. Rochow, 213 pp., 2nd ed., 1951, University Microfilms Inc., Ann Arbor, Mich., 1965; and, if he wants to concentrate on the useful materials, proceed to the book called simply *Silicones*, by R. N. Meals and F. J. Lewis, 267 pp., Plastics Application Series, Reinhold Publ. Corp., New York, 1959; or *Silicones and Their Uses*, by R. R. McGregor, 302 pp., McGraw-Hill, New York, 1954. An excellent and particularly thorough counterpart in German is W. Noll's *Chemie und Technologie der Silikone*, Verlag Chemie, Weinheim, 1960. The reactions of organosilicon compounds, with particular attention to their kinetics and mechanisms, are summarized by C. Eaborn in *Organosilicon Compounds*, 530 pp., Butterworths Sci. Publns., London, 1960. A comprehensive discussion of the preparation of organosilicon compounds is given in a Russian book now available in an English translation entitled *Synthesis of Organosilicon Monomers*, by A. D. Petrov, B. F. Mironov, V. A. Ponomarenko, and E. A. Chernyshev, 492 pp., Consultants Bureau, New York, 1964. The ultimate reference work in the field, and one which includes a register of every organosilicon compound that has been made (together with properties and references to the original literature), is the three-volume work in English by V. Bažant, V. Chvalovsky, and J. Rathousky entitled *Organosilicon Compounds*, Czechoslovak Acad. of Sciences, Prague, 1965.

These references will take the serious student to a rather high level of understanding about the metalloids, probably high enough to start research, if he likes. In order to keep up with what other people are doing, he will want to consult the current chemical journals of inorganic chemistry, and, of course, *Chemical Abstracts.* In order to make it easier to keep abreast of recent developments, mention should finally be made of three periodicals which feature topical summaries by experts: *Progress in Inorganic Chemistry*, edited by F. A. Cotton, Interscience, New York, annual volumes 1959– , *Advances in Inorganic Chemistry and Radiochemistry*, edited by H. J. Emeléus and A. G. Sharpe, Academic Press, New York, annual volumes 1959– , and, more recently, *Advances in Organometallic Chemistry*, edited by F. G. A. Stone and R. C. West, Academic Press, New York, annual volumes 1964– .

INDEX

SUBJECT INDEX

hydrides, 34–36
hyperpure, 54
iron alloy, 53
monoxide, 53
oxygen bonds, 54, 70
solid-state devices, 19–23, 93
Silicone polymers, 34, 54, 64–72, 92–94
bibliography, 102
history, 65
oil, 68
resin, 69–71
rubber, 67, 68, 96
synthesis, 65–67
Siloxanes, 58, 59, 64–72, 93, 96
Silver, 13, 25, 79, 84
Sodium, 33, 38, 61, 62, 86
Sodium chloride, 25
Solar cells, 26, 55, 85, 93
Solid-state electronic devices, 19–23, 93, 96
Space exploration, 93
Steel, 53, 86
Stibine, 78
Structure by x-ray diffraction, 42
Sulfanilamide, 82
Sulfur, 4, 34, 74
Sulfuric acid, 74
Superconductors, 13
Syphilis, 81

Talc, 59
Tellurium, 7, 25, 26, 29, 33, 35, 84–88, 97

forms, 86
organic derivatives, 86–88
uses, 86
Temperature coefficient of resistance, 10
Terramycin, 82
Tetraborane, 46, 49
Tetrasilicate ions, 56
Theory of bonding in metals and metalloids, 14–17
Thermochemistry, 89
Three-center bonds, 42, 48, 49, 101
Tile, 63
Tin, 16, 17, 39, 77
Transistors, 22, 23, 93, 95, 96
Tridymite, 60
Trimethylborane, 90
Trimethylchlorosilane, 66
Tripropylborane, 91
Trisilicate ions, 56
Trypan red, 80
Type metal, 78

Vitreous oxides, 33

Water glass, 56
Wave function, 43
Willemite, 56

Zinc, 9, 33, 75, 76
Zircon, 56

AUTHOR INDEX